# A to Call ADVENTURE

*OTHER BOOKMAKERS' BOOKS FOR YOUNG PEOPLE*

*The Weighty Word Book*
      Paul Levitt, Douglas Burger and Elissa Guralnick
      Illustrated by Janet Stevens, hardcover, 114 pp.

*The Silver Trumpet*
      Owen Barfield
      Illustrated by Josephine Spence, hardcover, 128 pp.

*Papa's Story and Other Tales*
      George MacDonald
      Illustrated by Don Borie, hardcover, 128 pp.

# A to Call ADVENTURE

## Hillary Hauser

Preface:   Joe MacInnis, M.D.

BOOKMAKERS GUILD, INC., LONGMONT, COLORADO

Published in 1987 in the United States of America by
Bookmakers Guild, Inc.
1430 Florida Avenue, Suite 202
Longmont, Colorado 80501

*Printed and bound in the United States of America*

Library of Congress Cataloging in Publication Data

Hauser, Hillary.
    Call to adventure.

    Bibliography: p.
    Includes index.
    1. Adventure and adventurers.      I.  Title.
G525.H323      1987      904      87-70932
ISBN 0-917665-18-X (pbk.)

*Cover design by Bob Schram*

*This book
is
for Jim Marshall*

OTHER BOOKS BY HILLARY HAUSER

*Women in Sports: Scuba Diving*

*The Living World of the Reef*

*Book of Fishes*

*Diamonds* (poems)

# Contents

# Acknowledgments

A book like this would not be at all possible without friends—the friends who invited me along on their adventurous escapades, the friends who laughed with me through the difficult moments and the friends who told me their wild stories. There are the friends who managed to listen to my own tales and encouraged me to write them down. In particular, Hadda and Chris Swann went overboard reading and rereading the beginnings of this book manuscript years ago. They put their foot down on the "Foxtail" version, as we called it, and they encouraged me to revise, rework, and try again.

Many of these stories have been published partly or completely in various magazines and my own books. Most of the stories in this book are original manuscripts, versions of the adventures I really wanted to see published, but which never were. I would like to acknowledge the publications where some of these writings have appeared in part or total:

"Gold in Them Thar Hills" ("River Gold", *New Zealand Dive Magazine*, October 1986); "Spanish Galleons and Long Lost Treasure", ("Diving for Treasure", *Redbook Magazine*, February 1978); "Ed Link: Trapped Beneath the Sea" ("Edwin Link: Triumphs and Tragedies", *Skin Diver Magazine* (November 1973); "Cousteau: The Mystique and the Magic" ("Cousteau—on the Cousteau Society", *Skin Diver Magazine*, November 1974, "The Cousteau Society", *Santa Barbara Magazine*, June 1977, and "Calypso Capers", *Westways Magazine*, September 1978).

# ACKNOWLEDGMENTS

"Sons of Cousteau: Carrying On in the Wake" (*Santa Barbara News-Press*, October 6, 1986); "Ron & Valerie Taylor: Getting to Know Sharks" (Hillary Hauser, *Women in Sports: Scuba Diving*, Harvey House, New York, 1976, and "Sharks!" *Santa Barbara Magazine*, February 1982); "The Sinkholes of Australia" ("Exploring a Sunken Realm in Australia", *National Geographic Magazine*, January 1984); "From the Jaws of Death ("Life after Jaws: An Appreciation of Sharks", *Oceans Magazine*, June 1983); "Devil's Hole" ("Devil's Hole", *Skin Diver Magazine*, December 1982).

Carleton Ray: Marine Revolutionary" ("Profile: Carleton Ray", *Skin Diver Magazine*, December 1978); "Eugenie Clark: Shark Lady" (Hillary Hauser, *Women in Sports: Scuba Diving*, Harvey House, New York, 1976, and "Profile: Eugenie Clark", *Sport Diver Magazine*, Spring, 1979); "Sylvia Earle: Aquanaut" (Hillary Hauser, *Women in Sports: Scuba Diving*, Harvey House, New York, 1976; "John Lilly: Searching the Unsearchable" (*Santa Barbara News-Press*, June 28, 1982); "Robert Ballard: Finding the Titanic" (*Santa Barbara News-Press*, November 17, 1985); "Sir Edmund Hillary: In the Face of Fear" (*Santa Barbara News-Press*, July 8, 1984).

"Down the Tubes in Hawaii" ("Down Hawaii's Volcanic Tubes", *Santa Barbara Magazine*, January 1987); "Conclusion: The Greek Medallion" ("Island Odyssey", *Westways Magazine*, March 1978).

These writings have been given a new heartbeat and life with the careful aid and assistance of Normandi Ellis and Barbara Ciletti at Bookmakers Guild, Inc. These two were unceasing in their encouragement and help—and sent flowers when things got a little too adventurous, even for me.

There is Denise Iest to thank, too, for never complaining as she typed day and night for hours and hours, and for her exceptional organizational talents and gathering of research materials; David "Spinucci" Tibbles cooked for us when the nights were far spent; Vince at On-Q Productions worked on photographs for no charge. The following also jumped into the project with enthusiasm and photographs: Al Giddings, Jack McKenney, David and Annie Doubilet, Bob Evans, Bob Marx, Hannes Keller and Margery Spielman. Jean-Michel Cousteau wired me some encouraging comments from Europe and took me to lunch one afternoon where we talked about the glories of adventure and the pain of climbing Mt. Mismi.

Finally, there is Jim Marshall to thank, because he made me stay in my room until I was finished.

# Preface

There is nothing so restless as human beings. We are continuously on the move, searching, reaching out, seeking new frontiers. For the best, and sometimes the worst of reasons, we are always heading toward the horizon. We have wandered all over the planet. We have climbed mountains, marched through jungles, staggered across deserts and snowshoed over the tundra. In all our travels, no place has so captured our imaginations as the sea.

Perhaps it is because of its size; it is the planet's largest single physical feature, covering two-thirds of the surface. Perhaps because it is a metaphor for our inner selves, a fluid symbol of unplumbed human depths. Whatever the reason, the ocean has always been one of those places where human beings could most vigorously express their restlessness.

Within the ocean are the beginning and end of life. It was here, billions of years ago, in the shallows next to a tropical shore—with its warmth, salinity and sunlight—that the great restlessness began. At each stage of development—protein, cell animal, man—it re-expressed itself.

The ocean is such a physiologically seductive place that most of the earth's two million species of animals and plants live on or under its surface. And in the past few decades, another form of life has taken up temporary residence in the deeps, *Homo sapiens,* or as he has been recently called, underwater man.

Here, at last, was the final intimacy. Human beings, pursuing the ancient urge, went down into the depths to work, to study, to see what it was like.

But there was a cost. The physical and chemical laws of this dark, airless, cold, high-pressure place were demanding. If precautions were ignored, death—

by embolism, asphyxiation, narcosis, hypothermia or decompression sickness—was near at hand.

I wandered onto the uncertain stage of deep diving in the early 1960s. I was a fresh-cheeked graduate from medical school. It was that delectable period near the start of a young man's life when he has nothing to cling to except his unmanageable dreams and nowhere to go except all over the place.

It was a compelling time. Jacques Cousteau was living in his manned station under the Red Sea. The United States Navy, dazed from the loss of the nuclear submarine *Thresher* with129 men on board, was piecing together a new manned undersea program. The edge of the sea was crowded with men whose ambitions and zeal were aimed at the depths.

Looking back over the last two decades, one is struck by the undiminished enthusiasm of the old ocean restlessness. In research laboratories and in the sea, information about the physiological effects of hyperbaric exposures has slowly built up. The human body works well at a depth of 500 feet and reasonably efficiently at 1,000 feet. It is able to tolerate, with some minor detrimental effects such as micro-sleep, direct exposures to depths of 2,000 feet.

In the North Sea and Gulf of Mexico, divers have worked in underwater stations for more than a month. Diving bells, decompression chambers and small submersibles have been developed as protection from the cold, pressure and wetness of the deep. Today, equipped with remotely piloted vehicles and protective suits, the old restlessness is in full flourish.

In the last two decades, we have penetrated deeper into the ocean, physically and intellectually, than any other generation.

In 1970 I turned my attention to a specific part of the ocean. It was the frozen sea on the roof of the world—the least known and most hostile stretch of water: the Arctic.

For over ten years, we have been carrying out three different kinds of under-ice diving expeditions. The first was a series of human performance studies, in which we assessed the technical problems of operating under the ice. How do we stay warm? How do we avoid getting lost? We evaluated suits, breathing systems and underwater lights. We made *in situ* measurements of heart rate and skin temperatures. We visited the North Pole and made over 500 dives in the water between Alaska and Greenland. In one of our lighter moments, we broke open a bottle of champagne in *Sub-Igloo,* the world's first manned underwater polar station.

The second series of expeditions was under-ice studies of natural history. Carrying lightweight cameras and high-speed film, we dove at various sites in the Arctic, including Pond Inlet, Point Lay, Kolucktoo Bay and Pangnirtung, to record the marine life under the ice. We made the first films of beluga whales, harp seals and narwhals. During one encounter, north of Alaska, 28 miles from shore, swimming under the polar ice pack, we came face to face with a 500-ton bowhead whale—and rediscovered the value of fear.

Our third series of expeditions was focused on maritime history. In 1853, a three-masted British barque, the *Breadalbane,* was crushed by ice off Beechey Island in the Northwest Passage. She went to the bottom in 15 minutes, in near-freezing waters, suspended in the luminous darkness beneath the ice.

In 1980, after three years of arduous searching, we found her almost intact. Two of her masts were still standing. She was sitting on the ocean floor in 330 feet of water, her big wooden steering wheel motionless, her compass unmoving, her keel pointing toward England and home.

Like any historical discovery, the *Breadalbane* beckons to the mind for a voyage of speculation. In the shadows of the ghost ship beneath the ice are hints of the old restlessness. And hints of our past and future.

In the years since the sinking of the *Breadalbane,* there have been hundreds of significant events, including the American Civil War and the founding of a dominion. They are years that saw the invention of the automobile, the telephone and the jet plane; and in medicine, countless advances, including the discovery of antibiotics and the development of open-heart surgery.

All being well, we can be certain of unique forms of the old restlessness. New technologies will bring more automation, more computers and faster communications. We will devise new relationships with energy—coal, oil, wind, water and the sun—using them in ways undreamed of today. And now that we have touched the moon, space colonies will soon be a reality.

A hundred years from now, technology will have dramatically changed the human environment. But the people will be the same; they will have the same passions, fears and frustrations and be endowed with the same outward-looking exuberance. The urge to explore the sea is part of the same creative quest that inspires research in medicine or in molecular physics; only the tools are different.

Restlessness is what this book is about. Hillary Hauser, a wonderful writer, a friend of all of us who have devoted our lives to the sea, has done a splendid job of looking at some of the ``sea people'', as well as other adventurers, and telling us what makes them tick and sometimes tremble. On these pages she has captured the second generation of underwater explorers who took the flame ignited by men like Jacques Cousteau, Ed Link and George Bond, and lifted it a little higher. In a clear, concise style she introduces you to a collection of larger-than-life characters who decided against ordinary careers and chose instead the unpredictable, unplumbed depths.

Hillary, always a good writer, has done it again. Here in her latest book are curiosity and compassion, a little bit of fear and a lot of perseverance. Here are old yearnings, new discoveries, men and women out on the noble edge, seeking the travail and triumph of the unknown.

Working in the ocean has been a revelation. Being down there, where it is cold and dark, and being afraid, alters one's views of the divisions and dualities by which we steer our lives. There is the discovery that both the ocean and the human body are triumphs of natural engineering, each a seamless web of physiochemical processes, stunning in their beauty and diversity.

There is the discovery that long outward journeys are inward ones, too, into the mysterious regions of the human heart. And those things that matter—love, wisdom and courage—lie nowhere else.

Finally, there is hope—for as long as humans endure, they will be graced by divine restlessness. As H. G. Wells wrote in his book, *The Shape of Things to Come*:

> For man . . . no rest and no ending. He must go on . . . at last across the immensity to the stars. And when he has conquered all the deeps of space and all the mysteries of time—still he will be beginning.

*Joe MacInnis, M.D.*

# Introduction

———

*The day shall not be up so soon as I,*
*To try the fair adventure of tomorrow.*

—*Shakespeare*
*King John V*

Adventure—what a magic word!

By it one enters into worlds previously unseen and unknown. It is the key to individuality, the courage to chart one's own life and the strength to remain separate from popular tides of thinking. When one decides to be an adventurer—or, more correctly, when one learns that he *is* an adventurer—he has committed himself to trying something new and different, something that has never been done by anyone else, at least not in the same way as it has been done before.

To be adventurous does not necessarily mean that one must execute a physical feat. Some of the greatest adventurers of all time have changed the world while staying in the solitude of their rooms, allowing only their minds to travel. The innovative scientist, writer or philosopher, for example, constantly tests himself against the unseen elements and hazards of fixed thinking, having enough courage to take a stand uniquely individual in his chosen field of thought.

The type of adventurer we can become depends upon the degree of our curiosity—how much we want to learn about something we don't know, how much we want to test ourselves against the forces of nature or the obstacles that stand in the way of the discovery that we are sure exists even though we can't see it. The unknown world we choose to discover may be the North Pole or the bottom of the sea, or it may be at the bottom of pages and pages of calculations or words. Even if someone else has been there before, discovered the thing before, perhaps we'll try to get there by some other way, or perhaps we'll simply do the thing alone, to prove that we can do difficult things by ourselves.

The word adventure means "hazardous and striking enterprise, a bold undertaking." We are all adventurers of a sort. In our youth, we have all been imaginary explorers at least. We might have, for an afternoon, hidden in a nearby wood, an empty lot or alleyway, all by ourselves and imagined that we were exploring a remote corner of the world for the first time. In these imaginary explorations, we may have dreamed of what we would do with our time, free of restraint and with ourselves as the only decision-makers. We would see the woods as an Amazon jungle, the empty lot as the Sahara Desert and the alleyway as a path to Shangri-La.

In these imaginary explorations are seeds of adventure, our wish to try something new and different by ourselves. Our only equipment may be our own two feet and the sandwiches our mothers made us for lunch.

In these early times away from home, however, we probably learned fairly quickly that successful adventures take planning, careful thought and unending perseverance. When we were children, we quickly abandoned our secret hideouts the moment dinnertime rolled around, whereas in an adult adventure, one gives up many dinners.

Perhaps all adventurers are perpetual runners-away-from-home—away from the conventional and away from the idea that "it can't be done." Christopher Columbus was certainly running away from the idea that the earth was flat, and he was not afraid to sacrifice himself, as well as his dinner, to prove his idea. Adventure involves sacrifice—for the very definition of adventure means that; although the end results are not guaranteed, one goes ahead anyway.

The element of chance that makes up the core of adventure is well illustrated in an advertisement placed in the *London Times* by the great explorer Ernest Shackleton, who was looking for people to join his expedition to the South Pole. He wrote:

> Men wanted for hazardous journey, small wages, bitter cold, long nights of complete darkness, constant danger, safe return doubtful. Honor and recognition in case of success.

Whether it's exploring the South Pole or the North Pole, whether it's climbing the highest mountain in the world or diving for sunken treasure, such risks are worthwhile to the true adventurer, because staying behind in the world of comfort and certainty means stagnation and restricted thinking. To paraphrase the words of the immortal Shakespeare, adventurers know they must take the tide when it serves, at the risk of being left behind in the shallows of ordinary thinking.

However, to a true adventurer, a curiosity unexercised is an impossibility. Curiosity drives an innovative thinker to do something about it, and curiosity does not go away by itself.

In fact, the adventurer may find that in actuality, he or she IS the adventure. That's because each one has a unique approach to every possibility on the planet, and how an individual perceives a thing or a challenge is what makes the challenge unique.

In examining the lives of people who have made significant contributions to mankind by the experiments and risks they chose to undertake, we can see that the Call to Adventure has been irresistible for each one.

The adventurers in this book serve as examples of what happens when someone decides to go ahead no matter what—past fear of death and of failures. In their own ways, these adventurers unlocked the previously unseen secrets of earth and of their own minds. Their lives inspire us, giving us more courage to follow our own convictions and to explore more fully our own ideas. Those who carve their own trails, rather than walking in the footsteps of others, are the leaders of this world. They are the men and women who think for themselves, whose wish to know about something previously unknown is stronger than the elements of nature or the probability of financial or physical ruin. Even when experiments don't turn out happily, when one could easily lose faith and make a hasty retreat back to port, the adventurer pushes on.

This irresistible propulsion is a common denominator in outstanding adventure stories and in the characters of the men and women who lived them. It propelled Hannes Keller to dive to 1,000 feet 13 years before anyone else did, and it inspired Sir Edmund Hillary to conquer Mount Everest. It pushed Rodney Fox to conquer his fear of the thing that had hurt him so badly—the great white shark.

Many adventurous escapades are born when one simply wants to find something that will enlarge his bank account—sunken treasure or river gold, for example. But even in these cases, the challenge of looking for the treasure is usually a bigger reward than the treasure itself.

Any of us can enter the slippery realm of chance—whether it's trying something new on canvas with a paintbrush or hiking a steeper trail on a nearby mountain. Any attempt to do something new and different offers new perspectives on life, and our willingness to stick with an original plan usually determines success or failure in what we set out to do.

Think of it! For all Columbus knew, his three ships could have disappeared over the flat edge of earth into eternity, but he sailed on. That took not only curiosity and conviction, but also courage.

Why not be courageous? Each of us can exercise a unique brand of courage no matter what our subject of interest may be, and every one of us can make a difference in this world with what we do. With the technologies and opportunities available to us today, we can do so much more with our curiosities than ever before, and certainly, we can do more than we did when we were children, when the only option we had for striking out on our own was to run away from home until dinnertime.

In my travels and day-to-day life, I have often lectured to or held roundtable discussions with young people who have expressed to me their innermost dreams and desires. I have talked with young girls who want to be astronauts and boys who want to be race car drivers. I have talked to budding poets and painters, philosophers and pilots. The seeds of these young desires may be great or faint, but they are there. I try to listen, to see what these aspirations are, and to help these youthful aspirers bring their dreams out into the light of reality.

Too often, these dreams are lost before they are realized. Too often, these seeds of aspirations are dulled by the world of worry—worry about mortgages, life insurance and all the things "everyone is supposed to do." Sylvia Earle, an aquanaut featured in this book, called these adult-induced fears the "Great No" that many well-meaning parents impose on their children: the "Don't do this, don't do thats". She felt fortunate that her own parents encouraged her romantic meanderings in the woods, which eventually developed into a full career as a scientific explorer. Similarly, Eugenie Clark expanded her world from early observations at a New York aquarium to important discoveries about sharks and other fishes. And Sir Edmund Hillary insisted on climbing mountains, all while he was keeping beehives in New Zealand. Usually, it takes extra effort to follow an adventurous trail while keeping a full-time job. Adventure does not mean shirking one's responsibilities.

I assembled this book in the hopes of encouraging young people to follow their dreams. By looking at the lives of successful people, we gain encouragement for our own endeavors. Many of the stories have been individually published in books, magazines and newspaper accounts I have written over the years. When I considered the stories as a group, I saw a common thread throughout: the courage to proceed no matter what doubts others cast upon a particular course of action and careful listening to one's own dreams and desires in the early stages of life.

I've included, too, my own adventures, offered to me through my career as a writer and chronicler of events. For me, writing is the key that lets me into other people's lives, which is an adventure in itself, and writing has allowed me to seek experiences, just so that I could relate them to others. In my youth, I spent hours gazing at the ocean, writing poems to sea lions and kelp. I didn't remember this until many years later, when I was earning a reasonable living as a writer about ocean-related subjects and when someone asked me when I began my career.

At the same time, I also realized that my brother, Craig, now a successful builder in Arizona, spent his childhood building treehouses, forts and rafts. Similarly, my sister, Merrily, now a longtime, dedicated mother, had spent much of her childhood playing with dolls and bossing my brother and me around.

All of which has led me to the conviction that within every young thought are the seeds of later fulfillment. These budding ideas *must* be listened to, not only by parents and teachers, but by the young person thinking them. A young person is never too young to take responsibility for what he or she wants to do in life, even when there are many everyday chores and responsibilities to fulfill.

In his Pulitzer Prize-winning biography, *Profiles in Courage,* the late John F. Kennedy talked about courage needing no exceptional qualifications, magic formula or special combination of time, place and circumstance. "It is an opportunity that sooner or later is presented to us all," he wrote.

He also pointed out that the exercise of courage often requires sacrifice.

> In whatever arena of life one may meet the challenge of courage, whatever may be the sacrifices he faces if he follows his conscience—the loss of his friends, his fortune, his contentment, even the esteem of his fellow men— each man must decide for himself the course he will follow. . . . The stories of past courage can define that ingredient—they can teach, they can offer hope, they can provide inspiration. But they cannot supply courage itself. For this each man must look into his own soul.[1]

Many of the stories of courage and outrageous daring in this book are tied to the ocean in some way or another, and that is because the road to the sea is a direct route to a deep, undefinable mystery that has touched almost everyone at one time or another. It is my sincere hope that my telling of these stories will reveal how adventure can unlock the mysteries of the planet, both undersea and on land, and that the tales will encourage readers to begin today to listen to themselves, to dare to be different—to answer the Call to Adventure.

**Notes**

1. John F. Kennedy, *Profiles in Courage* (Harper & Row, New York: 1956), pp. 216-217.

*Chapter 1*

*Dick Anderson*

# Gold
# in Them Thar Hills

The trail to Canyon Creek snakes its way for a mile down the side of a steep, heavily wooded canyon in the Sierra Nevadas, California's mother lode country. It is so steep you can touch ground with your uphill hand without bending over, and if you lose the trail you are liable to fly down the entire mountain by the seat of your pants. I know this is true because I flew down half the mountain toward Canyon Creek by the seat of my own pants until I was stopped by a tree. The thick layer of dried pine needles and leaves made the slope as slippery as ice, and since no one had been on the trail for what looked like months, traction was nonexistent. My knees shook uncontrollably as I looked down the rest of the hill into the dark of the canyon. There was only one way to stay on the path and that was by watching closely for the old blaze marks that had been chopped years before into the thick bark of ancient pine trees by hopeful seekers of gold.

The man I had just married was a reincarnated forty-niner, a seasoned adventurer who had an uncanny knack for finding gold. That June morning in 1968, Dick Anderson's internal calendar sped back to the year 1849, when thousands of fortune-seeking adventurers descended on the California mother lode to search for gold.

This Canyon Creek trip introduced me to the slippery world of treasure, where men scratch, blast, dig, dynamite, pump and drill their way through river banks and sea beds in search of the great something-for-nothing. Dick had

*Courtesy of Keene Engineering, Inc.*

*Launching the expedition in the California River.*

access to a mining claim in Canyon Creek, which is near the North Fork of California's Yuba River, east of Sacramento on Highway 49 outside Downieville. He hadn't been to Canyon Creek in years. It was here that he and his friend Donald Carter spent every summer years before. The two of them fared pretty well at Canyon Creek. Dick even came away with a sizeable amount of nuggets to show for his work. Then Carter fell down a mine shaft in Nevada and died. That cooled Dick's gold fever, but only for a time. Gold-seekers have a history of such disasters and accept them as part of this glittery game of chance. Dick could hardly wait, in fact, to start digging again once he made up his mind to it.

Before starting down the trail to the bottom of the canyon we had checked in with Cliff Laurent, the deputy sheriff at the Cal-Ida sawmill near the top of the trail. This stop was required by law. If we accidentally ignited a forest fire, there would be a clue as to who did it, but more importantly, if we didn't check out after a reasonable length of time, someone would come looking for us. As I slipped and slid down the trail behind Dick, I wondered if Cliff Laurent would really go to all the trouble. I was convinced that no one could *ever* find us. Our Volkswagen bus had been carefully buried in the trees so that the bears wouldn't eat it; and right then I was sure that they'd skip the bus anyway and head out to snack on us. In that place we were so alone that I couldn't help but think how easy it would have been to disappear off the face of the earth without anyone knowing it.

Our dog Igor was having a fine time. A poodle-terrier mix, Igor was hardly a dog of the woods and feared everything, but as a trail scout he did fine. He ran ahead and back in a fraction of the time it took us to navigate one way. I would stop to rest while Dick tried to find the overgrown and faded blaze marks. Igor would run off, run back, run in little circles, look out into the deep woods, look worried and then whine. I identified with him a lot, but I never said a word. New brides always want to be good sports.

On my back I carried a lot of the groceries and some of the diving gear. Dick hauled more of the diving equipment, plus pans, picks, supplies, gasoline and more groceries. On top of it all, he dragged a mattress behind him, saying that since no one had been to the cabin in five years, any leftover supplies would be gone, used by stray fishermen or prospectors—or eaten by the rats. He was sure that the rats had eaten the mattress that had been left there. These rats were ferocious, he said, and from everything I heard about them I figured they might have eaten the cabin itself. Bus-eating bears and cabin-eating rats: this had to be the mother lode version of *The Call of the Wild* and I was Buck, stolen from my comfortable home and pressed into service as a trail beast.

When I saw the cabin I was greatly cheered. It sat back from the creek, 100 feet or so, up a little trail in the trees. It was the real live log kind that measured about 15 by 20 feet, and it had a creaky wooden door crowned with a set of old reindeer antlers at the top. A single window faced the river. Just outside the door was a tiny dirt terrace and on its uphill side was a wood-burning stovetop set into rocks. There was still a neat stack of old wood underneath a rickety workbench to the right of the stove. The river in front of the cabin formed a deep pool that was cold and crystal clear, and Dick said it was full of trout.

I looked at everything and felt much better. Igor wasn't so sure. He kept backing up and growling and I half expected something wild to leap out of the woods and attack us. Animals are supposed to have uncanny instincts about other animals lurking nearby, so I was always watching Igor's displays of uncanny instincts. The only trouble with this alarm system was that Igor was deathly afraid of things like falling leaves and rolling stones, and by this time he had become a bundle of dog nerves.

The inside of the cabin was a wreck. Even though the supplies had been hung from the rafters years before so that the rats couldn't get at them, the vermin had found plenty of other things to chew on. The entire room was a rat's nest. Everywhere we looked was shredded paper, cloth, bits of this, piles of that, pine needles, wood chips nibbled and chewed. Dust and dirt covered the wood plank

Courtesy of Keene Engineering, Inc.

*Diver scans bedrock for seams of gold, which are often covered with surface soil.*

Courtesy of Keene Engineering, Inc.

floor, and the crude shelves that held big glass jars of five-year-old rations were covered with rat trails.

Igor growled and backed up from the door. Had I known what he was trying to tell me I might have growled and backed up, too.

In about four or five hours we had the cabin completely swept and cleaned, our new supplies in, the old ones out, thrown on the rubbish pile at the far end of the outside terrace. The crowning touch was when Dick installed the mattress on top of the old, rusty bedsprings. Igor wasn't taking any chances and immediately rushed up on the bed and didn't move for the rest of the day or evening.

Before dark we lugged in several pails of water from the river for cooking and washing, and took a brisk swim in the freezing, clear pool in front of the cabin. Then we set about cooking dinner, which was some magic thing that expanded from a small box onto a mismatched pair of tin plates. This, together with boiled river water, was as wonderful as cordon bleu and champagne—all because we were in the woods.

That night, Dick hung his revolver on the tree-limb bedpost and turned down the kerosene lamp until it went out. Igor was asleep at my feet and I was feeling quite fine. I was blissfully tired and almost dropping off to sleep.

Suddenly the bedsprings began to rattle furiously. I sat straight up and Igor disappeared down the crack between the bed and the wall.

"Dick!" I said. "What's that?"

"Don't know, just a minute."

He fumbled around in the dark. The bedsprings rattled again, more violently this time.

"Iggy, where are you?"

The bedsprings rattled again.

"Rats," said Dick. "I can't find the matches."

Whatever was making the springs rattle like that had to be a gorilla.

"Hold on, I found them."

Dick lit the kerosene lamp and when the light came on I was instantly horrified. Sitting on the cross beams of the wall at the foot of the bed was the biggest rat I'd ever seen. Its eyes glowed in the light of the lamp and it looked at us, transfixed and evil. I was speechless.

Dick, being a reincarnated forty-niner, knew exactly what to do. He reached for his revolver. The rat was immediately dead. Then Dick holstered the gun and turned off the light.

I was stricken by dumbness undefinable. The dog jumped back up to his place at my feet and I was now supposed to go to sleep. There was no way on

Courtesy of Keene Engineering, Inc.

*Diver with dredge and sluice at work.*

earth I could close my eyes. I lost every shred of blessed tiredness I had earned and I lay there in the sleeping bag bed, stiff as a board, the image of that splattered rat indelibly etched into my brain. I was alone for what seemed like hours with the image of that rat.

What I hadn't learned yet was that rat-shooting is nothing when you're looking for gold.

For the next week Dick and I sniffed and sniped, which are two ways of picking around for river gold. A sniffer, which sort of resembles a giant turkey baster, will suck up any flakes or small nuggets that might be stuck in the cracks of a river bed. More often we sniped, using a fireplace poker to scrape out the cracks and crevices.

Gold that is found in rivers and streams is called placer gold (a word that rhymes with plaster). Essentially it is gold that has been getting stuck for millions of years in the natural riffles of the river bed—the cracks, crevices and deep potholes. Dick taught me how to spot likely looking cracks for gold—cracks which run from one side of the river to the other, but which are hard to spot because they are often covered with surface soil. We could usually see some part of them if we traced them carefully from either side of the river. Once we located such a crack, we'd put on our masks and snorkels, and dip our heads underwater for a

*Courtesy of Keene Engineering, Inc.*

look. The water was only three or four feet deep in the area we were diving, but it was always swift. If I got swept away, Dick advised me to relax and enjoy the ride until I got to the nearest falls. At that point, he said, I should start worrying.

Once under water we'd snipe the loose dirt and sand from the crevice into the gold pan. The gold pan was the essential tool. All the excavated sand and gravel went into it, and when we had collected enough of it, Dick would begin to pan. Panning is done just like in the movies. Dick dipped the pan into the river, then swirled and dipped again and again, to wash off the top layer of sediment, picking out the larger rocks and dipping again. When he finally reached black sand at the bottom of the pan, I was leaning over him like a hawk. Suddenly I realized I had caught a little of the thing called gold fever. When a few tiny chips and flakes of gold appeared I shrieked as if we'd unearthed Fort Knox.

A few chips and flakes were not enough for Dick, so one morning he dug out the old rusty parts of his dredge from inside the cabin. Dredges are called "suckers" among gold divers, because they are essentially underwater vacuum cleaners that quickly remove all the overburden—the sand and gravel which sits on top of bedrock where the gold is trapped. Our dredge had a lightweight metal vacuum tube at one end and a sluice box with the riffle tray at the other. When the dredge was fired up, water ran through the sluice box and into the riffle tray at the

7

*The sluice and riffle tray eliminate sand and mud, allowing gold to get caught in the coarse metal mesh.*

other end. The dirt, sand and gravel shoveled into the sluice box were sent through the riffles in a wash of mud. Any gold in the sand and gravel would sink down and get caught in the coarse metal mesh. With this dredge Dick and I were ready for some big nuggets.

With a sluice box and dredge we didn't bother with turkey basters or fireplace pokers. We used shovels. We first had to find a likely looking spot where gold might have settled into the bedrock, and the likely looking spot we picked was within the roots of a big tree near the river bank. Dick set up the dredge and connected up the pump, and we both proceeded to dig. And dig. We shoveled so much dirt into that sluice box that I was sure we would reach China by noon. I developed a severe case of blisters and so I volunteered to serve as cheerleader, watching over the riffle tray for signs of color. I have to admit I became a fickle hunter of gold. By the end of the afternoon I had taken up trout fishing instead, using a jar of iridescent orange salmon eggs as bait. It turned out to be a great day for me. I ended up with four trout. Dick ended up with a hole the size of a mass grave, a set of rippling muscles and toughened hands.

By the end of our adventure in the woods, I had become an excellent trout fisherwoman, sniper and digger of holes; and I hadn't been swept over the falls. Dick and I left Canyon Creek with one small vial of flakes, not enough to pay for the gas we'd fueled the dredge pump with, but one has to be a good sport about such things. One has to be a good sport, also, about climbing a mile out of a steep canyon. Hiking down that trail was rough, but it was child's play in comparison to the hike up. Each step was a deep knee-bend and we performed hours and hours of them.

Igor was the happiest dog I'd ever seen. He repeatedly ran up ahead of us and back with cheery barks. On one hand, I think he was reminding us that there are some advantages to being a dog—like having four legs—and on the other hand, I think he was letting us know he was glad to get out of the woods and back to the city. Sometimes dogs just have no sense of adventure at all.

Dick and I went to Canyon Creek several times during the next few years. It always seemed just enough gold appeared to make us go back for more, but never enough to make us believe that we went for the gold alone. I finally realized that the value of gold was not the sole reason for seeking it, but that the act of looking for it propelled me. If a man is lucky enough to strike gold, it is a near mystical indication that he is favored by the Hand of Fate. The dice are not always rolled for fortune alone, but because man likes to test himself on many different levels.

When I first started going to Canyon Creek I was a young bride out for a spree in the woods, accompanying a husband who had a nose for gold. I didn't know then that in all that digging the seeds of adventure were being planted within me, seeds that would bloom later when I was no longer with him and during times of choice between the safe and the uncertain. In these later years, I opted more and more for the uncertain, because I sensed that, like gold, the richest experiences of life were often in a hidden lode just beneath the surface of the obvious.

9

*Chapter 2*

Hannes Keller

# Hannes Keller
# and the 1,000-Foot Dive

---

*A fool is a man who never tried
an experiment in his life.*


— *Erasmus Darwin*

---

annes Keller is a Swiss version of the mad scientist, a mathematical genius with unruly hair, a Cheshire cat smile, and mischievous eyes that crinkle up when he laughs about the next wild scheme he has in mind.

His wild schemes are numerous. For example, he attempted to design a better deep sea diving suit and designed, instead, the tight-fitting ski suit that eventually adorned the bodies of Spider Sabich and the Swiss Olympic ski team. He once premiered a pianist who couldn't speak, he said, but who would play from unpublished manuscripts by Mozart and Beethoven. Keller circulated the rumor that the manuscripts had been given to the pianist years before by some obscure Russian count who had found them in his attic. Then, in a Zurich concert hall which was jammed with music lovers and music experts from all over the world who were curious about such a find, Keller took the stage at intermission and announced that the compositions were really those of the pianist. The whole exercise, Keller said, was to prove that music critics didn't really know what they were talking about. Great talents exist, he said, whether critics recognized those talents or not.

Keller's biggest schemes, however, had to do with diving and deep ocean exploration. In the late 1950s, he made a 750-foot dive to the bottom of a Swiss lake using something that resembled an upside-down garbage can. While *Life* magazine, the press and other media from around the world waited on the boat for him to surface, they talked about how his technology would revolutionize

11

undersea exploration and boost the offshore search for oil. Meanwhile, Keller, deep in the lake and out of sight of everyone, was literally sick from fear, trying to figure out how to cut the weights off the inverted garbage can so that he could rise to the surface again.

Scientific exploration is sometimes like that. Giant leaps forward for mankind do not always involve complicated technologies, but sometimes only someone willing to try something new and take the risks. In the field of diving, Keller was the human guinea pig of all time. He constantly pushed himself to go deeper, faster, by using the deep-diving formula worked out by Dr. Albert Buehlmann of the Zurich Hospital. Finally Keller got deep enough and every oil company in the world began to watch what he was doing. Deep-diving technology and oil exploration go hand in hand because oil platforms do not normally go in water where human hands cannot reach valves and flanges.

In 1962 Keller and Buehlmann announced that they were ready to make a dive to the incredible depth of 1,000 feet. No one believed it at first, but then Shell Oil agreed to finance the experiment and the dive was on.

Buehlmann, a longtime researcher of the effects of pressure on the human body, had worked up an unusual plan wherein the diver would make a very rapid descent to the bottom, faster than anyone had ever dived. During the ascent a variety of gases would be switched on at various depths to facilitate a return to surface pressure. The gases themselves were kept a secret, but the rumor was that one of them was argon. Keller and Buehlmann stood to earn a lot of money from the oil companies for their formula, so they were not broadcasting the particulars from the rooftop. By the time the dive took place, the mounting curiosity had finally given way to chicanery. Keller believed someone had drilled one of his air tanks during the night to get a sample of the chemical contents inside.

In 1969, seven years after that famous dive, Dick and I went to Switzerland to research Keller for a book that Dick was writing about the Swiss adventurer's life. At that time, Keller was still a national hero in Switzerland. He had done a thing long before anyone had ever considered doing it and no one had yet broken his 1,000-foot record. It was like having Neil Armstrong land on the moon while the Wright brothers were trying to get their first airplane off the ground. The 1,000-foot record, unbroken until June 1975, meant that Keller was about 13 years ahead of his time.

While the 1,000-foot dive attracted attention for its success, there remained the awful fact that two people had died during the course of it. Dick was the logical writer to explore what actually happened during the dive because he had been one of the safety divers. He had, in fact, been credited with saving Keller's life.

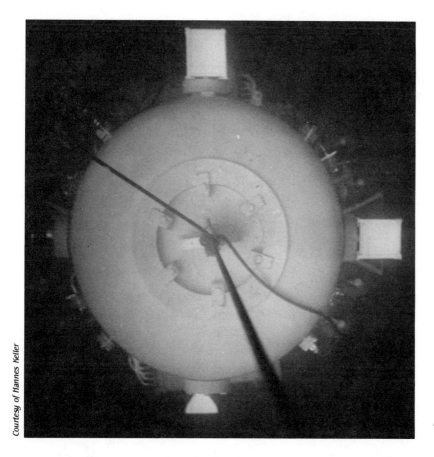

Courtesy of Hannes Keller

*Atlantis diving bell underwater during descent.*

The dive itself took place off Catalina Island, California, in the deep ocean trench that lies just off the island. Keller's vehicle was the diving chamber *Atlantis.*

On the day of the dive, the press and a few members of the public gathered aboard a surface vessel. Two safety divers prepared themselves for any emergency that might arise. The divers were Dick Anderson and Chris Whittaker. In retrospect, no one could figure out why there were only two safety divers, but hindsight is always sharp when a disaster occurs.

British photojournalist Peter Small was Keller's diving companion. When all was ready, the two of them got into the chamber and the hatch was closed. The *Atlantis* was hoisted over the side of the support ship and made a rapid plunge to the bottom. At 1,012 feet the divers opened the bottom hatch, walked out several feet from the chamber and planted the Swiss and American flags on the bottom. Then they quickly returned to the chamber to be hauled back up. Keller says they both knew that they would lose consciousness when they opened their masks to breathe the air in the chamber, but they had been instructed that they

13

would regain consciousness later on as they were being hauled to the surface. Therefore, in spite of the temporary effects, they were to open their masks anyway.

As it happened, Keller opened his mask first and immediately passed out. Then, said Keller, Small took one look at his unconscious friend and froze. When the chamber was raised, Small eventually lost consciousness anyway, but he wasn't breathing the air inside the chamber. Somewhere along the way he began to embolize, the air bubbles inside his body expanding as the outside pressure decreased.

When the diving chamber reached just about 200 feet, the surface crew noticed it was not pressurizing properly. If they continued to hoist the *Atlantis* back to the surface, they ran the risk of giving both divers either a bad case of air embolism or the dreaded bends. The surface team, at this point, was unaware of Small's condition.

Dick and the other safety diver, Chris Whittaker, were dispatched to investigate and make sure the bottom hatch was closed. They swam to the chamber, checked it thoroughly, found the hatched closed and went back to report to the surface support team what they'd seen. On the way up, Whittaker inflated his buoyancy vest and at the surface, someone noticed that his nose was bleeding. Dick indicated that they had seen nothing wrong with the diving bell, but was told the chamber was not pressurizing, therefore, something had to be wrong. Since they were the only safety divers available, Dick prepared to dive again. Whittaker was ordered out of the water. Instead, he took his diving knife, slashed his vest to deflate it and followed Dick back down to the chamber.

This time Dick could see bubbles escaping from the bottom hatch of the *Atlantis*. Going around the entire circular seal, he discovered what may have been the tip of a swim fin, caught in the hatch and holding it open a fraction of an inch. This would have been apparent on the first dive, but for some reason the diving chamber was not pressurizing at the time Dick and Whittaker were viewing the bottom hatch.

Dick motioned to Whittaker for his diving knife, and Whittaker gave it to him. Dick used the blade to push the obstruction clear of the seal. The hatch closed completely, but the seal still leaked. Dick pulled down on the hatch and motioned for Whittaker to swim to the surface, to give the signal for the chamber to be hauled up while Dick stayed and held the hatch to make sure it sealed. Whittaker signaled that he got the message and started up.

Dick waited and waited. His decompression meter was entering the red zone, meaning that he had overstayed his limits and might get a good case of the bends if he ascended without stopping near the surface for decompression. Fortunately the leak had stopped because the different pressures inside and

*Courtesy of Hannes Keller*

*The Atlantis diving bell being lowered off Catalina.*

outside the chamber had shifted. Dick went straight for the surface. He didn't have the air to decompress, so there was no stopping on the way up. There is a theory that some people get the bends less easily than others. Dick appeared to be one of those people, because once on the surface, he showed no signs of decompression sickness whatsoever.

The minute Dick surfaced, however, a crewman asked him the horrible question: "Where's Chris?"

Chris Whittaker was never seen again.

The chamber was hauled the rest of the way to the surface with the hatch successfully sealed. Keller regained consciousness and began an intensive resuscitation attempt on Peter Small, but the British photojournalist was dead by the time they got the hatch open. Keller suffered no ill effects at all.

The Keller dive was an awful paradox. It was a success because one man had made a 1,000-foot dive and lived, proving that the mysterious mixture of gases

15

had worked. It was also a disaster because of the deaths involved. No one knew whether to cheer or boo. The effect was the same as if Neil Armstrong had landed on the moon and lived, while fellow astronaut Buzz Aldrin had not made it back to Earth. In that case, would the moon landing have been considered a success or a failure?

In the case of Keller's dive, no one knew for sure. Some press reports called him Hannes *Killer,* while others denounced him for not sharing his secret gases and dive formula with the scientific community. However, soon after the dive, Buehlmann had, indeed, published the details of Keller's dive, although few people had ever read the paper. Scientific papers tend to circulate only among scientists who know where to find them.

The diving community ignored everything and called Keller a hero. So did the Swiss. However, upon investigating the accident, the Los Angeles coroner's office credited Dick for saving Keller's life. So, Dick was a hero also.

Dick's book project meant conducting many interviews, and there were many conflicting stories that caused him a lot of second-guessing and creative headaches. While Dick and I were in Switzerland, he talked with Keller's associates and friends and I listened to the sublime wonders of Keller at his Steinway piano. He was, and is, a magnificent pianist.

The book on Keller was never finished because Dick felt he couldn't sort out the absolute facts of the dive without question. I continued to correspond with Keller over the years, and in 1973 I saw him again, when he came to California for a large diving congress in Anaheim. Since this was his first visit to America after the days of the 1,000-foot dive, I invited some people to my home to meet him, including Scott Carpenter, the U.S. astronaut who, at the time, was an aquanaut in the Navy *Sealab II* program; Dr. Joe MacInnis, who was to be the first man to dive underneath the North Pole; Paul Tzimoulis, publisher of *Skin Diver Magazine,* and also Goldy McJohn, my neighbor who was also the piano player in the Steppenwolf rock group.

Keller and I decided to play the piano for our guests, and once we got going we couldn't stop. He played Beethoven and Bach and I played Brahms and Liszt. We played Schumann and those wonderful nocturnes of Chopin. His performance was breathtaking. No one spoke or moved after we stopped. They had witnessed the passion in Keller that spills out into his music, much as it does into his adventures. I have since learned that adventurers often have a deep love for artistic things like music—because art is an extension of a consuming curiosity. The art of the great masters is immortal because the curiosity reaches genius proportions and emerges amid ordinary thinking as a shining light in the world.

The last time I saw Keller, at the beginning of 1981, he was building deep-diving chambers to be used in the North Sea oil fields, diving suits, instruments

Courtesy of Hannes Keller

*Keller with the computers.*

for decompression and other devices for deep-sea diving operations. From there, he transferred into the challenging world of computers, designing an unusual software package that translates one language into another. Keller's "Witchpen" software corrects spelling even as a person types into a computer. It is, Keller said, the first computer program of its kind. These two inventions have created an international business for "Hannes Keller Witch Systems" with subsidiaries in Germany and the U.S.

At his main office in Zurich, Keller keeps a grand piano so that he can play his classical music while his staff of 12 assembles the softwares of his design. For Keller, designing something no one else has thought of before represents the ultimate challenge and he continues to mix this challenge with his art.

That his 1,000-foot record was not broken for 13 years after his *Atlantis* experiment, Keller has never stopped to consider. A world record was not his interest.

"When I do something I try to be good and do a professional job, and always remember that 50 percent of my business is fighting the inevitable risks," he said. "But I would feel utterly ridiculous if I tried to be the record-setting mad scientist for the rest of my life. Actually, I want to have an interesting life, that's what I want. I am the man looking for the right mix of all to get me into the depth of life. That's really my thoughts on life, so that at the end of it, I can say it was worth it to have had it."

## Suggested Reading

Robert Marx, *Sea Fever* (Doubleday & Company, Inc.: New York, 1972).

## Chapter 3

*Bob and Jenifer Marx*

# Spanish Galleons
# and Long Lost Treasure

In 1655 King Philip IV of Spain ordered an armada to sail from Cartagena to Spain by way of Havana. One of the armada's flagships was the *Nuestra Señora de la Maravilla*. The treasure aboard the ship included gold, silver, jewelry, pearls, emeralds and other precious stones. In addition to these valuables, the cache included a solid gold statue of the Virgin Mary holding the Christ Child. When the *Maravilla* set sail, her cargo was worth more than five million pesos.

On January 4, 1656, somewhere near the Bahama Channel, the *Maravilla* ran into shallow water and hit a reef. A second ship rammed the grounded *Maravilla* and, less than an hour after the collision, the galleon began to sink. There was a frantic attempt to rescue the 650 persons aboard the ship, as well as the treasure, but by the time the disaster was over there were only 45 survivors. All of the treasure sank with the ship.

In the years to follow there were repeated attempts by Spanish divers to salvage the lost treasure, but only about one-quarter of it saw the light of day. In time the wreck was covered by shifting sands, and most of the treasure belonged to the sea, hidden with the ship.

In 1972 we came along.

Dick and I were living on Catalina Island when Bob Marx and Willard Bascom invited us to join their expedition to find the *Maravilla*. Bob Marx is a marine archaeologist and treasure diver from Florida; Willard Bascom is an oceanographer from California. We knew both Bob and Willard well and had great respect for them, but the amount of gold and treasure that promised to emerge from such an expedition made the idea seem even better. The search would begin by early summer, based out of Fort Pierce, Florida.

Dick was beside himself with the perfectness of the whole thing. He flew to Florida right away to join Bascom and Marx. I was to meet him later.

Since we would be gone indefinitely on this hunt, Dick found Igor the dog a new permanent home. This broke my heart, but I learned that one makes sacrifices in the name of adventure. Besides, Igor was promised an adventure of his own. The poodle-terrier chicken of the woods would soon be chasing rabbits in the desert of Hesperia, California, sleeping in haystacks and getting pelted with buckshot from suspicious gun-toting neighbors.

It is important to know who you are sailing with on expeditions such as this, because once you are at sea, that's it. If a feud starts, there is no way to take a walk. Knowing what I did about Bob Marx and Willard Bascom, I figured we were all in fairly smooth waters.

Bob Marx is a salty character who had helped the governments of a number of countries (including Spain, Lebanon, Panama and Colombia) locate and salvage ancient shipwrecks. He spent four years excavating the sunken city of Port Royal, Jamaica, which disappeared beneath the sea in 1692, but had to quit when one of the underwater buildings collapsed on him and injured his back.

Marx is a prolific writer and raconteur of tales so adventurous that his hearers sometimes find it hard to believe anyone could lead such a life. In 1962 he sailed an authentic replica of Columbus' ship *Niña* from Spain to San Salvador. For this voyage he was dubbed Knight Commander in the order of Isabel the Catholic, which means he is an official "Sir". What bothered Marx the most about the *Niña II* expedition was that since they were making every last detail of the voyage authentic, he had worn bloomers along with his sword and tights when the *Niña II* arrived in port. If there is anything Marx can't tolerate, it's being mistaken for a sissy.

After the *Niña II* voyage, he tried two Viking expeditions, both of which failed when their authentic ships sank. Ever since then, he had been hankering to build an authentic replica of a Phoenician ship and sail it from Lebanon to Mexico.

In 1960, while digging around in the archives of Seville, Marx learned about the *Maravilla*. He figured roughly where the wreck would be from old nautical charts and the written reports of one survivor of the 1656 disaster. With this information in hand, Marx set about the business of getting financial backing and the divers to go after the ship.

Willard Bascom became Marx's partner in the deal. With Marx, Bascom formed the Seafinders Corporation and together the two men raised $200,000 to finance the hunt. Bascom always had a fascination for ancient wrecks, and looking for them seemed to be about the only thing he hadn't yet done in the ocean.

Bascom already had a significant reputation and had written several books about the sea. His *Waves and Beaches* had involved extensive mapping and surveying of the entire U.S. coastline for defense and strategic purposes. It is now an often used textbook in college oceanography courses. *A Hole in the Bottom of the Sea* chronicled his incredible plan to drill into the Mohorovicic discontinuity— that layer of rock between the earth's crust and mantle. The Moho, as it is called, has some peculiar properties which were discovered and defined by the Croatian scientist Andrija Mohorovicic. Bascom wanted to know what sort of material this Moho contained.

He developed the idea of drilling what he called the "Mohole" at sea in an area where the earth's crust is thinnest. He devised the revolutionary concept of dynamic positioning, wherein the unanchored drill ship could be kept stationary during drilling by firing up four propellers (called "steering screws"). This would keep the ship centered over the drill pipe. While John F. Kennedy was president, the Mohole project proceeded full force, but when Kennedy was assassinated in 1963, the new administration discontinued funding for Mohole, and the project was scrapped. Still, the scientific achievements were enormous. Bascom considered it a mixed glory.

So, in May of 1972, Dick had completed all the preparations for the *Maravilla* expedition with Bascom and Marx. He phoned me from Florida and said that all was ready and I should come as soon as possible. I met Rhoda Bascom, Willard's spirited Norwegian wife, in Long Beach and we began our three-and-a-half-day drive from California to Florida. The drive itself was an adventure. Every state contained unique people and varied landscapes.

Summer in Florida was something else. I thought I could adjust to any weather in the world, but by the time I'd been in Satellite Beach for a week and hadn't slept one night because of the heat and humidity, I knew I was in trouble. We were living with Marx, and so were the Bascoms. Marx's wife, Jenifer, was enormously congenial about it all. A red-headed, vibrant, intelligent and fascinating woman, Jenifer was in the midst of a pregnancy and was not going with us on the expedition. Later I regretted that, because with her wits, Jenifer might have been able to smooth the troubled waters that were to erupt around us.

Our ship, the *Grifon*, was an old, converted trawler outfitted with prop blasters, which are giant metal tubes that fit over the ship's propellers to deflect water downward. They also scatter sand to uncover such things as shipwrecks.

21

*Photo by Dick Anderson*

*Diver Hillary Hauser spots a resting anchor (right).*

*Hillary swims along the full length of a huge anchor (opposite page).*

The *Grifon* was no yacht, but it was perfect for what we were doing. After several days of hunting around for last-minute supplies and groceries, we left Fort Pierce and headed out for the Little Bahama Bank.

The way to find sunken Spanish galleons is easy, if you know how. Marx leased a proton magnetometer, an expensive piece of equipment, and we had a speedboat. Marx and Bascom had obtained a salvage lease from the Bahamian government for a 25-square-mile chunk of ocean that lay 25 miles from Memory Rock and 45 miles north of West End, Grand Bahama Island.

Treasure hunting goes like this: day in and day out you cruise up and down imaginary aisles of ocean with a speedboat and the magnetometer, watching the instrument for any signs of unusual activity. Usually there are none. Marx mentioned it might be difficult because the sunken *Maravilla* had 58 bronze cannons aboard and bronze does not register on magnetometers. There was also a lot of difficulty with the magnetometer itself. Marx jokingly—yet not entirely jokingly—blamed its erratic behavior on the fact we were working in the Bermuda Triangle, that notorious area where electronic equipment goes haywire and where sailors, like ourselves, disappear.

On the days we didn't use the magnetometer, we towed each other behind the boat, alternating among Dick, Bob and me. In this manner we were like shark

Photo by Dick Anderson

bait being trolled. It didn't make me feel any better to see that that Dick always carried a speargun when he was on the line, whereas I was never offered any means of defense. In any case, we could scan the bottom visually this way, looking for the telltale sign of shipwrecks—any abnormal-looking pile of too-regular stones. Round ballast stones were used in galleons for weight distribution and ballast. Such stones did not corrode or erode.

Mainly the whole thing was tedious. Treasure hunting does not get good until you actually find the treasure. Until that point you travel up and down, up and down, back and forth, back and forth, day in and day out, over rectangular chunks of ocean. Whenever we picked up a reading on the magnetometer, we stopped to investigate, free diving first to see what the area looked like. If the preliminary searching resulted in anything at all interesting, the *Grifon* was brought over and stationed above the area with three anchors—one off the bow, two off the stern— then the prop blaster was lowered. When the engines were put into forward gear the boat wouldn't move, but the enormous thrust of water jetted straight down and blew away mountains of sand underneath the boat.

We uncovered a number of old anchors that way, one of them with an ancient wood stock still intact, protected over the years by the sand that had buried it. It was a shame, in a way, not to keep these anchors, but if we'd salvaged every

*Courtesy of Mel Fisher*

*Mel Fisher displays gold and silver Spanish treasure (right).*

*Bob Marx aboard the Grifon with Maravilla treasure on the deck (opposite page).*

artifact we found, the *Grifon* would have looked like an overloaded trash barge. We were out there, after all, for gold doubloons.

Cabin fever is one of those things you hear about, but I had no idea how far it would go. We were all respectable people, or at least we thought so in the beginning. Bob Marx began to dispel his anxieties by telling wild tales, and the rest of us either got into or escaped from one another by jumping overboard for a swim.

The heat was oppressive. Even at sea there was no respite from the overwhelming humidity. I soon discovered that I could get temporary relief by sticking my head into the freezer, but that made it worse when I had to return to normal atmosphere. Night after night I didn't sleep, and neither did Dick. Marx was tough, seasoned to Florida, and nothing seemed to bother him. My bunk lay just below a porthole, but we were not allowed to open portholes when the boat was under way at night. I found out why one night when I opened the porthole above my head and seconds later was drenched with seawater. Since the staterooms were below deck next to the engine room, the sleeping quarters of the *Grifon* were impossibly stuffy when the boat was moving. I finally took to the stern deck and slept inside the speedboat, which wasn't too bad once I wedged myself down between the seats.

One morning, at about 5 a.m., I was sleeping fitfully when I was awakened by the sound of sails flapping. I sat up and saw that a sailboat had pulled alongside

the *Grifon*. Our captain heard them, too, and came out to give them audience. Unbelievably, it was a couple in their early sixties out on a pleasure sail.

"Where're we at?" the man yelled.

They were in the middle of the Little Bahama Bank, out in the Gulf Stream, 40 miles from the nearest land, with no idea of where they were. I began to understand about the Bermuda Triangle. People didn't disappear in extraterrestrial fashion, they simply got lost. Pleasure sailors from Florida head out to sea toward the Bahamas and other Caribbean islands with little idea of navigation, believing that it's just a "short hop" between here and there. Indeed, it is a wide expanse of ocean that has to be reckoned with. Boats do not always come by so regularly to help you if you lose your way. When I first boarded the *Grifon* I was given the serious instruction that if I ever walked outside while the boat was under way I had to always, *always*, tell someone I was doing so. One slip over the low rails of the boat without anyone being aware of it meant that you might just swim in circles until the sharks found you. I took that advice very seriously, and when I went out on deck at night I crawled on all fours.

About mid-July we had to run from Hurricane Agnes.

This hurricane demolished a lot of the eastern coast of the United States. Out at sea the wind was nasty business. We beat a hasty retreat to West End Bahamas and for three days we waited it out. The storm didn't ease the tempers that had been brewing during the previous weeks. By the end of Agnes, it was Dick vs.

*Clear water and strong sunlight accentuate the graceful features of the dolphin (also on opposite page).*

Photo by Dick Anderson

Bascom, Bascom vs. Marx, Marx vs. Dick, Dick vs. me, and Marx vs. himself. We dived almost daily, and I loved that. When you're underwater you don't hear people talking.

One day an incredible thing happened. We were moving the *Grifon* from one place to another when a group of porpoises appeared at our bow. They swooped around the old trawler with a happy vitality—rolling, diving, gleefully crisscrossing each other in the waves.

I really wanted to get into the ocean with the porpoises and asked the captain to stop the boat. Bascom and Marx put up an immediate protest. I told Marx I wanted to get in with them and take some pictures. He reluctantly agreed—mainly, I think, because he thought it would be an exciting story when the porpoises killed me. They didn't. Then everyone jumped in—including Bascom.

We dived to the bottom, 30–40 feet, and the porpoises came to us, circling around and surfacing when we did. The big males, the mothers and babies, all played the game of swimming fearlessly close, but staying just inches from our reach. The dolphins lifted my spirits immeasurably. Every time they came around I wanted to jump in with them, and most of the time I did. Some years later I did a fair amount of research on porpoises and wrote several articles about them. It was only then that I became convinced that the porpoises on this trip were the real treasure.

Finally, Dick decided to leave the expedition.

When we got back to Fort Pierce, we gathered our things, drove down to Key West and visited Mel Fisher, a successful treasure hunter who had founded the Treasure Salvors museum. We met him in his office, and he confided that he was on the trail of the *Nuestra Señora de Atocha,* which had gone down in 1622, 40 miles southwest of Key West in the Marquesas Islands. The *Atocha* was the ultimate gem of Spanish galleons, Fisher said, having 40 tons of treasure aboard. He described to us a 63-pound bar of silver among the items reported missing in the ship's manifesto, or cargo list. Mel told us all this and then popped the question to Dick: did he want to head another salvage Fisher had going—the 1715 fleet that had gone down off Florida, for $125 per month and 1/600th of his empire?

"Heck, no," said Dick, "we're getting out of here!"

Some days later we flew out of Florida, and two weeks after we were back in California, Marx and Bascom found the *Maravilla.* In the first month, they brought up over $5 million worth of treasure.

About ten months later, Fisher found the *Atocha.* Although a positive identification of the wreck wasn't made until some time later, his crew began to bring up treasure that eventually added up to $400 million.

When Mel's salvage operation was in full gear, his wife Dolores and sons went to work with him. Dirk Fisher was in charge of the salvage barge *Northwind,* and Kim Fisher captained the second barge *Southwind.* In May, 1973 the divers picked up the anchor from the galleon and followed a trail of silver coins, muskets, swords and iron cannonballs until they reached a pocket of treasure that yielded an incredible 1,500 coins in one day. The divers called this spot "The Bank of Spain." Some time after, Dirk located the pilot's astrolabe, an ancient instrument used for charting celestial bodies and which predated the sextant. This valuable artifact had been made in Lisbon about 1560 and was perfectly preserved because it had remained buried in deep sand all those years.

The divers then found two gold bars, a four-and-a-half-pound gold disk and silver bars stamped with identifying numbers and initials. In the cargo lists of Spanish galleons the numbers of silver ingots are recorded, and treasure expert Eugene Lyon was able to make a positive identification of Fisher's wreck. It was definitely the *Atocha.*

Then trouble began. While a *National Geographic* film crew was on site documenting Fisher's operation, the son of one of the photographers was swept

Photo by Dick Anderson

*Hillary Hauser encounters two dolphins from the school (below).*

Photo by Dick Anderson

29

*Dolphins can frequently appear to be standing upright, as they swim in the sea.*

Photo by Dick Anderson

into the propeller of the *Southwind.* He was flown by helicopter to Key West, but died before he reached the hospital.

Soon after, the Securities and Exchange Commission received a complaint about Treasure Salvors, Fisher's company. While auditors investigated Fisher's records, he couldn't sell stock or shares of treasure, which all but closed down his operation as the stocks and shares were his main source of funds for the expedition. To give an idea of the expense involved in such an operation, by the time the *National Geographic* magazine article was published in June 1976, Fisher had found a reported $6 million in treasure, but had spent $2 million bringing it up.

When the complications with the SEC were finally unravelled, the State of Florida raised its hand for 25 percent of Fisher's find. Fisher maintained that the *Atocha* lay outside state jurisdiction, but during a first division of the treasure Florida acquired the precious astrolabe. The Supreme Court finally decreed that the *Atocha* did, indeed, lie outside state boundaries.

Now the federal government plunged into the fight, claiming it had jurisdiction over the wreck. Fisher filed suit in Federal Admiralty Court for ownership of the *Atocha* treasure. In 1976, three years after Fisher's discovery, the Federal Admiralty Court ruled that the U.S. government had no claim to the treasure of the *Atocha*. This was a great victory for Fisher, but the victory was marred by another accident that proved to be Fisher's biggest heartbreak.

In July, 1975 Dirk Fisher, his wife Angel, and six other persons anchored the *Northwind* somewhere near the Marquesas atoll for the night. Early the next morning, while everyone aboard was asleep, the *Northwind* began taking on water and suddenly capsized. Three people were drowned: crewman Rick Gage, and Dirk and Angel Fisher.

Numerous legends speak of evil spirits that guard hidden treasure. Montezuma is said to have put a curse on the fabulous Aztec fortune to ruin the men who seek it. Those who search for sunken treasure know both the imaginative tales and the realistic risks. Still they search, because somehow they feel their fortunes and fates will differ from all those who have gone before. By the time they've lost friends, battled the courts, faced death and suffered tragedies as great as Mel Fisher's, they usually learn they are just as frail as anybody else.

## Suggested Reading

Robert Marx, *Shipwrecks of the Western Hemisphere,* (The World Publishing Company: New York, 1971).

Willard Bascom, *Waves and Beaches* (Doubleday: New York, 1964).

Willard Bascom, *Hole in the Bottom of the Sea* (Doubleday: New York, 1961).

Eugene Lyon, ``The Trouble with Treasure'' (*National Geographic Magazine,* June 1976).

Duncan Mathewson III, *Treasure of the Atocha* (E. P. Dutton: New York, 1986).

Peter Throckmorton, *Shipwrecks and Archaeology* (Little, Brown and Company: Boston, 1969).

*Chapter 4*

*Ed and Marion Link*

# Ed Link:
# Man-In-Sea

*They that go down to the sea in ships,*
*That do business in great waters,*
*These see the works of the Lord*
*And his wonders in the deep.*


*— Psalms*


In 1974 I was on Catalina Island, aboard the ship *Swan* and watching the filming of the ABC television movie, *Trapped Beneath the Sea*. Lee J. Cobb, playing the part of diving pioneer Ed Link, was watching two divers being lowered on a commercial diving platform from the side of the ship. The divers, Bob Meek and Jock Menzies, were playing the parts of Navy rescuers attempting to free Link's submarine, the *Johnson-Sea-Link*, which had become trapped on the sea bottom at 350 feet. Inside the submarine were four other divers, and one of them was Link's son, Clay. Time was running out for the trapped men.

The Hollywood movie was a re-creation of a real-life tragedy that occurred on June 17, 1973. In the actual incident, Navy rescuers had failed to act quickly enough, and Clay Link and Al Stover had died in the back of the submarine. In that real-life version, Meek and Menzies had been the pilots of the *Johnson-Sea-Link*.

As I watched these two play the part of the Navy divers, I found it an extreme irony that the survivors of the tragedy now played the part of those who had failed to rescue their friends. That two men lived while two men died was a result of circumstances I had known well because I'd written a detailed account of the accident for *Skin Diver Magazine*.

I was chagrined to see that the Hollywood version of the disaster had included unrealistic romance and unnecessary drama. The submariners dramatized their fears of going into the deep as if they were doomed Jonahs sinking into the mouth of a bottomless whale. Their girlfriends emoted theatrically about relationships and danger. The script missed the deep and subtle drama of Ed Link's struggle—his life work at odds with the loss of his own flesh and blood. Even so, I was momentarily overwhelmed by the adventurous world of filmmaking, where the treasure is not gold, pieces of eight or Spanish galleons, but a mere seed of an idea that blooms into cinematic splendor.

The life and character of Ed Link needed no cinematic embellishment, however; the real thing was drama enough. Link was the originator of Man-in-Sea, a revolutionary underwater program that allowed divers to stay and work in the ocean for extended periods of time.

In the early 1950s, divers were limited to staying only a few short minutes underwater at a depth of 300 feet. Keller's dive in 1962 was the first attempt to put man on the ocean floor at 1,000 feet; but Keller and his companion, Peter Small, could stay no more than a few minutes at that depth. Ed Link was determined to find a way for divers to remain submerged.

The incentive came from the oil industry, because offshore oil platforms needed to reach into deeper water where new sources of oil were being discovered. Offshore platforms require human hands to work on the structures at depth for an extended time. The problem was in finding a way to prevent deep-sea workers from experiencing either nitrogen narcosis or the dreaded bends during the undersea work.

At depths below 130 feet, nitrogen in pressurized air causes a drunken feeling which usually renders any deep underwater work largely ineffective. At 300 feet a diver can easily lose consciousness completely.

In coming back to the surface, nitrogen, dissolved in the bloodstream during a dive, can turn into bubbles, much like the bubbles that are released when a bottle of champagne is uncorked. A bubble lodged anywhere in the body can cause the "bends", a painful and sometimes fatal paralysis. To allow the nitrogen to work itself out of the bloodstream, a diver must stop for a time at various depths in a programmed ascent called decompression.

Eventually it was discovered that divers could surface quickly, then enter a decompression chamber aboard ship where the pressure within is comparable to that of the diver's deepest descent. Then, the pressure inside the chamber is slowly brought back to normal again.

However, in the early 1950s, decompression techniques were not perfected. No one knew how long a diver could stay underwater without harm to himself. Hannes Keller had tried breathing different air mixtures to replace the nitrogen during his rapid descent and ascent, but these gas combinations proved nothing

Photo by Hillary Hauser

*Two divers being lowered into the ocean off Catalina.*

about prolonged diving time. It was still believed that if a diver stayed underwater at length, his decompression time could be days, or weeks.

Then, in 1957, U.S. Navy Captain George Bond discovered a physiological phenomenon that solved the problem. He found that after a time, the inert gases of the diver's air supply completely saturate the body tissues. After a while, the tissues cannot absorb any more inert gas, no matter how long the diver stays underwater. When the saturation point is reached, decompression takes the same amount of time, whether the diver has been down for two days or a month. Testing his theory at a U.S. Navy laboratory, Bond discovered that the total saturation time is 24 hours. Bond's discovery paved the way for Ed Link to take the theory and prove it.

In 1962 Link put diver Robert Stenuit in an aluminum diving chamber and lowered him 200 feet into the Mediterranean Sea. He stayed down 24 hours, proving that man could survive longer periods at depth underwater.

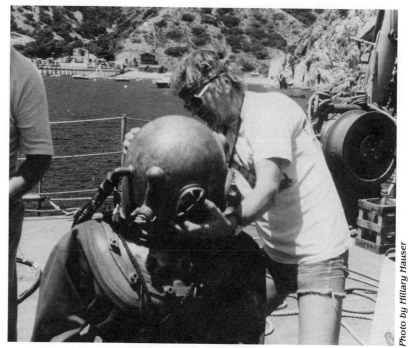

*Director Billy Graham helps diver Jock Menzies with his hard hat. (right).*

*Director Billy Graham conferring with producer Frank Capra, Jr. on the set of "Trapped Beneath the Sea." (opposite)*

*Photo by Hillary Hauser*

The saturation dive ushered in the era of Link's Man-in-Sea programs. Although others—including Jacques Cousteau and the U.S. Navy—were conducting similar experiments, Link persisted where the others held back. He launched SPID (Submersible, Portable, Inflatable Dwelling) in 1964. It was the forerunner of all underwater habitats. Robert Stenuit and Jon Lindbergh stayed in SPID for two days and nights at a depth of 432 feet. This was the longest and deepest dive man had ever made.

In addition, Link designed a special sea lift hydraulic crane, which led to the development of the first small diver lockout submarine.

In a lockout system, a diver enters a separate chamber in a sub, which is pressurized to the depth outside. Then the hatch is opened and the diver swims out. Later, he can reenter the chamber and be brought slowly back to surface pressure. With Link's hydrocrane, the entire submersible could be hauled aboard the surface ship before the diver reached surface pressure. Then the diver continued to decompress while the others exited the chamber.

*Deep Diver* was launched in 1967. With this the era of Man-in-Sea entered full swing. *Deep Diver* was entirely self contained and capable of reaching depths of 1,200 feet. When two divers locked out of this mini-submarine at 700 feet, it was a landmark in oceanographic exploration. But Ed Link was not through yet.

Photo by Hillary Hauser

With Seward Johnson he established the Harbor Branch Foundation, a marine science center backed by the Smithsonian Institution and based in Florida. Here he constructed through assistance, the *Johnson-Sea-Link*, a small submersible he nicknamed the "Bubble Sub." The *Johnson-Sea-Link* featured a transparent, acrylic, spherical chamber forward for unobstructed observation. An aluminum alloy compartment aft contained a hatch for lockout diving operations. Capable of diving to 1,000 feet, the *Johnson-Sea-Link* was considered Ed Link's crowning achievement.

For Link, the untried, uncharted path had been continually validated by sweet success. When a man tries something completely new, such validation is important, for by the successes he maps his course. But success itself is hard-earned. Sometimes the price is paid afterward in the form of unforeseen sacrifice.

Link's sacrifice was his son.

On June 17, 1973, in a project sponsored by the Smithsonian Institution, the *Sea-Link* made a dive to the scuttled destroyer *Fred T. Berry*, 20 miles off Key West. Aboard the *Sea-Link* were Clay Link, Ed Link's son, who was supervisor of Life Support Systems at Harbor Branch; Al Stover, an expert submariner; Jock Menzies, an ex-commercial diver and pilot of the sub; and Bob Meek, an ichthyologist and scientist working at Harbor Branch. Clay Link and Al Stover were stationed in the rear lockout compartment, while Meek and Menzies piloted the sub from the acrylic sphere in front. The two compartments were separate, with no passageway between.

At 351 feet, while trying to pick up a fish trap, the *Johnson-Sea-Link* became tangled in a cable from the *Berry.* The U.S. Coast Guard learned of the trouble and flashed a message to the Chief of Naval Operations in Washington: "Submiss/Subsink"—an official distress call that signalled the beginning of a tragic 36-hour ordeal.

The Navy sent its submarine rescue ship *Tringa,* which arrived by 4 p.m., about six hours after the first call for help. By 8 p.m., it had set up its four-point mooring, only to find itself 50 feet off position. The ship moved and re-anchored. By 11 p.m., they were in place.

Because there was no diving bell aboard the *Tringa,* the Navy dispatched its "Roving Diving Bell" from San Diego. However, by 3 a.m. the next morning, the divers had gotten within ten feet of the sub, only to report that they could see the *Sea-Link,* but do no more. The diving bell arrived and went down at 9:20 a.m., but the swift ocean current prevented proper placement of the bell. A second attempt was made at 1 p.m., but the bell reached a depth of only 300 feet, snagging on the *Berry* itself.

Meanwhile, inside the *Sea-Link,* the trapped divers tried to encourage each other via the communication system between the chambers. Meek and Menzies fared better in their front compartment than Stover and Link because they were insulated by their acrylic sphere. The aft compartment, constructed of highly conductive aluminum, grew cold and the cold proved fatal.

In an enclosed chamber, divers cannot rebreathe their own air, because of carbon dioxide poisoning which leads to blackout. However, baralyme, a powdery substance that scrubs carbon dioxide from the air, can be used, but it loses its effectiveness below 70°. The temperature in the back compartment was considerably lower than that. Later reports revealed that Stover and Link spread the baralyme over their bodies, hoping that their body temperatures would keep the baralyme warm enough to continue scrubbing carbon dioxide from the air.

Around 1 p.m., after the second rescue dive had failed, Meek and Menzies started to use the air from the emergency breathing system on the sub. By this time, Stover and Link had lost consciousness. A later report said that Stover, an expert submariner, understood that he and Link were not going to make it and turned off their air supply to give Meek and Menzies a better chance of surviving.

Joe MacInnis, a doctor of undersea medicine who had worked with Link in his early diving experiments with Stenuit and Lindbergh, flew down from Canada to keep watch with his mentor aboard the *Tringa.*

Finally, the commercial salvage vessel *A. B. Wood* sent down a Naval Ordnance Lab Sled to the site. The sled was equipped with television monitors and sonar, which located the trapped sub and guided a hook from the *Wood* to it. The *Wood* grabbed the *Johnson-Sea-Link* and hauled it to the surface.

When the hatches were opened, the rescuers saw that Link and Stover were dead.

The accident was an awful setback to the ocean fraternity, which watched the news, stunned. However, Link, in the deep of his darkest hour, said: "We've got to try harder."

To prevent such a tragedy from occurring again, Link and the Harbor Branch Foundation began building a rescue system to ensure that divers would never have to rely on other institutions for rescue. "This can make our future operations safer, as well as more helpful to others," he wrote, "as we all agree that we must learn to live with the oceans for our future developments."

He knew that the element of chance extends to every attempt to do something new and different. The price he paid for his knowledge was dear—the chance had taken the life of his son—but he forced himself to look forward, to improve the situation that had exacted his awful sacrifice.

### Notes

1. Personal correspondence to Hillary Hauser, November 6, 1973.

### Suggested Reading

Marion Clayton Link, *Windows in the Sea* (Smithsonian Institution Press: City of Washington, 1973).
Nicholas B. Zinkowski, *Commercial Oil-Field Diving* (Cornell Maritime Press, Inc.: Cambridge, Maryland, 1971).

## Chapter 5

Joe MacInnis, M.D.

# Joe MacInnis:
# Under the Arctic Ice

*Are you earnest? Seize this very minute!*
*What you can do—or dream you can—begin it!*
*Courage has genius, power and magic in it*

*Only engage and the mind grows heated,*
*Begin it—and the work will be completed.*


— *Goethe*

----

Underwater documentaries got their biggest boost in the late 1960s, when diving filmmakers put themselves in odd subsea circumstances and recorded the outcome. It was before the days of high-priced Hollywood films such as *The Deep* and before high-tech television documentaries were regularly issued by the National Geographic Society or the Cousteau teams. In those days, the underwater filmmakers of the world assembled once a year at the Santa Monica International Underwater Film Festival.

Later, when underwater filmmaking commanded high prices from Hollywood, these annual gatherings ceased. No longer could anyone afford to make low-budget, self-financed films when high-paying movie producers combed the streets, paying fortunes for underwater film services. The adventurous photographers who showed up yearly in Santa Monica constituted the only pool of subsea filmmakers in the world.

These were rare days. Usually, after the showing, everyone involved gathered to discuss their dreams for the future. Al Giddings, who had drifted through fast-current reef passages in Tahiti to film sharks, quietly talked about plans to film a very deep breathhold dive by Frenchman Jacques Mayol. (Giddings later filmed the underwater segments of *The Deep* and other Hollywood epics.) Stan Waterman talked about leaving the east coast for a year to take his family to Tahiti. (His project eventually became a National Geographic special.) Dick Anderson wanted to make another film about diving for treasure or gold.

During one of these festivals, I met the exuberant Joe MacInnis, an underwater medical expert from Canada. Joe had an adventure planned that was to eclipse everyone else's.

He would be the first man to dive underneath the North Pole.

In those days Joe entered into the room bursting with secrets, and he liked to astound people. He once grabbed a large wooden saber from a hotel wall, brandishing it in the air as he launched into one of his tales. He was always in the middle of something—excited, enthusiastic, energetic, full of ideas. However, writing was one of his favorite activities—something, he said, that made "getting up at 6 a.m. worthwhile." In 1971 his poetry book, *Underwater Images,* was published in Canada. It was followed later by *Underwater Man,* a high-voltage chronicle of his underwater experiments and expeditions; but largely it was a poetic tribute to the sea. Many other books came after.

I learned that Joe was more than a dreamer; he was and is a serious doctor. As a world-recognized authority on hyperbaric medicine, he served as a medical consultant to several of Ed Link's saturation diving projects, notably *Deep Diver.* He also served as medical consultant to the U.S. Navy *Sealab* project.

As president of Undersea Research, Ltd. in Toronto, Joe has been the catalyst for developing Canada's manned underwater programs. In 1970 he designed and installed Canada's first underwater habitat in Tobermory Bay. The habitat *Sublimnos* provided scientists with a base where they could conduct underwater experiments, a project that sparked Canada's interest in her 150,000-mile coastline and continental shelf.

When Joe turned to the underwater Arctic, he turned the world's attention to one of the least known regions of the planet. In 1972 he designed and launched *Sub-Igloo,* a spherical plexiglass underwater station which he placed beneath the ice in Canada's Resolute Bay, 600 miles north of the Arctic Circle. There, where winter temperatures averaged 45° below zero, MacInnis and his team made excursions to study human and equipment performance, as well as Arctic marine life. The expedition was documented by both the National Film Board of Canada and *National Geographic Magazine.* Between 1970 and 1974, MacInnis made four expeditions to the site so that the seasonal differences could be monitored. During one of these trips, Joe became the first man to dive beneath the North Pole.

Joe said that as a child he was fascinated by water. A common theme among underwater adventurers is the compelling interest that takes precedence over the plotting or planning of a career.

"I grew up in Ontario, a place with a quarter of a million lakes, and you can't go a mile without falling into the water," he said. "Each summer we'd go to the lakes, summer camp or something, and I fell in love with aquatics. I had this

Courtesy of Joe MacInnis

*Underwater partners, Dr. Joe MacInnis of Toronto, Ontario, and Remote Piloted Vehicle of Falmouth, Massachusetts. The vehicle, equipped with powerful lights and television still cameras, filmed H.M.S. Breadalbane, sunk in 330 feet of water.*

psychic alliance with water and a real love for it. I am a strong believer that kids are natural explorers, and it was then very normal for me to look at water and wonder what was on the other side. Then came the face mask; it suddenly became a new window."

His first career decision came in his early teens. "I decided, naively, that I wanted to become an Olympic swimmer," Joe said. "I went to Florida to a college swim clinic. At the end of it someone said, 'Hey, let's go diving!' I dove off Fort Lauderdale's second reef and it was one of the most exciting days I've ever had in my life. I was completely entranced with the rhythms and colors. That kind of watershed event plays a critical role in our lives. I think probably less so when you get older, but when you are young and *tabula rasa*, those magnificent imprints

43

are really strong, as this was on me. It was a rather shallow dive, but still full of all the glories of color, fish and life. I knew then, and I was still in high school, that somehow I had to work in the sea, that the sea had all the ingredients for me: exploration, discovery, self-discovery, artistry, creativity."

Because of this fascination, Joe entered the field of medicine. "I went through medical school, not with the idea that I wanted to become the classic savior doctor, but that medicine offered the best insight, the best telescope, into what was to me the most fascinating element of the planet—man: this incredible creature with all his fears, joys, delights, euphorias and sadness. Medicine was, in fact, a road map. As I went through college I kept hearing the names Cousteau, Link and (George) Bond, especially toward the end of my medical years in the early 60s. I thought if I could just work with any of them, I could combine medicine, the sea, and man, and they would all fuse into a very tight radius. Glory of glories! It came to pass."

At the time no university offered a degree in diving medicine. Joe was not stymied by the fact that he had become interested in something no one had thought of before. He knew his destiny was tied to the sea and that he would tie this to his studies in medicine. It meant he would have to carve a path no one else had trod.

"I knew I would probably have to go out of Canada, because nothing was happening there," Joe said. "Everyone said, 'Hey, there is no way. A doctor in the sea? What are you going to do, operate on porpoises? Eye transplants on sharks?' There was nothing to justify man and the sea, so it meant creating one's own curricula. The only way to do that was to go to the ultimate university—the ocean."

In 1963 Joe graduated, unsure of what was going to happen. He went to a meeting of the Underwater Society of America in Philadelphia. Here, he met George Bond, a U.S. Navy captain who had pioneered saturation diving techniques, and who was, therefore, called the Father of Undersea Medicine. Bond was preparing for the first of the U.S. Navy's *Sealab* projects, in which divers would live in an underwater habitat for extended periods of time.

Joe recalled his approach to Bond.

"I went up to Bond and said, 'Look, I just graduated from medical school and I'm just starting my internship and I really desperately want to work in the ocean with man, as a physician.'

"He looked at me and said, 'Son, we just can't do it. As much as I'd like to have you come with us, it's a Navy program and you are a civilian and you're from Canada, so it just isn't going to work.'"

Joe wasn't one to stop at discouragement; in fact, discouragement propels him to try harder.

"I realized I didn't know a thing, but figured I'd better get my humble shoes on and work like mad," Joe said. "I knew that it was going to cost me money but I thought if I could hang in there with enthusiasm for about five years, ten years, whatever, I could make it. There was no one else, no other physician, who wanted to work full time at this thing like I did."

His next opportunity came with Ed Link, who was dreaming of constructing an oceanographic facility at Harbor Branch, Florida, where submersibles took divers to the ocean floor for deep-sea studies. In those days, the challenge was to keep man underwater for ever-increasing lengths of time.

"I couldn't bring anything to him except a lot of enthusiasm and a little bit of experience," Joe said. "I now know how small it was. I pursued him for three or four months. Every couple of days I'd phone or write or wire. He was involved in the review of the *Thresher* tragedy and he was virtually inaccessible. There was no way I could get close to this man. I finally decided I had to resolve this thing, so I phoned him and said, 'Look, I'm going to be in Washington tomorrow and I must see you for just 15 minutes. I want to come and work for you and I know you're terribly busy, but would you talk to me for 15 minutes?' He said that he would see me at 9 o'clock the next day.

"It was then 4:00 in the afternoon. The simplest thing would have been to take an airplane, but there wasn't one. Toronto to Washington was a distance, so I drove all night. At about 6:30 a.m. I was passing through Gettysburg and hit a deer. It wiped out my radiator and the front of the car, and I was standing in the road with deer all over the windshield. I was going to meet with Ed Link in a couple of hours and all around me was nothing but graveyard and fog. It was ominous. So, I pushed the deer off the road and shoved the car in a ditch and walked back to Gettysburg and rented a car at 9 o'clock. I phoned Ed Link and said, 'Mr. Link, you're not going to believe this, but I'm going to be a little late and here's why . . .' He laughed, and I saw him at 10:30."

Joe said that when he met Link, he "let fly five years of ambition."

"I guess we hit it off," he said. "I think he could feel the intensity; I was terribly excited. At that time, he was looking for a guy who could support his deep dive series, Man-in-Sea, phase II. Link said to me, 'There is one thing you must do. I'll put you on a Link Foundation Fellowship and I want you to go to work for Chris Lambertsen. He is the best in the world. I want you to spend some time in his laboratory and get some training and have him introduce you into diving medicine as we know it.' I think working with Chris Lambertsen was the most exciting intellectual experience I've ever had. Chris is truly a giant among men."

Under Lambertsen's direction, Joe was assigned to work with another subsea technician, Dr. James Dickson. He prepared for the deep dives of Man-in-Sea by "getting the analyzers ready and finding out from Jim what the problems were."

45

"We did some mice experiments which ended up in a series of dives to 4,000 feet, which, for mice in 1965, was pretty exciting," Joe said. "The two of them, Lambertsen and Dickson, guided me and showed me some of the hurdles. At that time they were just starting to get ready with their new 1,200-foot facility. It was very exciting, because it was my first introduction into real diving research."

Joe's first practical experience at sea came in March 1964, when Link began the first tests for Man-in-Sea, phase II. In this program, two divers, Jon Lindbergh and Robert Stenuit, dove to 432 feet for 49 hours. It was, at the time, the deepest, longest dive ever made by man.

Joe called this dive his "entrance into the serious game." As a doctor, his role was to provide medical life support for Lindbergh and Stenuit. He remembered the implications of the dive's success.

"That was the first real demonstration that man could saturate deep within the sea and could go to 400 feet plus. By coincidence, we just happened to rest the station at the average depth of the continental shelf—432 feet. This demonstrated that man had the physiological resources to live for short periods of time at the deep edges of the continental shelf. We knew that if he could do it for two days, then he could probably do it for 20 days. It was a very pivotal experience, because it brought together a lot of different technologies. It fused deep diving engineering, physiology and operations together for the very first time. It also helped spawn a lot of commercial diving companies. Link was then able to go to Union Carbide and say, 'Look what man can do. Let's start a company, an ocean systems company,' and for a while, Ocean Systems was the largest diving company in the world and certainly the most advanced from a research point of view. Then, others came strongly on the scene, such as Comex and Oceaneering."

Joe went to work as an undersea medical director for Ocean Systems, where he worked on ways to get man deeper for longer periods of time. Bond's discovery that a diver could stay in a submerged chamber indefinitely without getting the bends had had enormous impact. The age of saturation diving was begun.

"We had the most incredible 24- to 36-month period where we had the research dollars that we needed, and the expertise that we needed, and we started simulation dives," Joe said. "We did several hundred dives in that period, including 48 hours at 650 feet. We began the first really deep oxygen-helium dives when the other guys had no idea what was going on past 200 feet in terms of saturation diving."

From 1965 to 1968 Joe worked with Ocean Systems. He also continued work with Ed Link on the *Deep Diver* projects out of Harbor Branch. Cousteau, who had

46

*Courtesy of Joe MacInnis*

*Joe MacInnis, Peter Benchley and Emery Kristof.*

introduced the world to diving, had, by this time, shifted into the area of film and, by 1965, the French captain had almost disappeared from the deep-diving arena. Meanwhile, the U.S. Navy had launched its *Sealab* program, in which astronaut Scott Carpenter played a role as an aquanaut.

However, the real push for underwater man was coming from the oil and gas industry, now drilling farther and farther offshore for oil. By 1969 offshore diving companies like Comex and Oceaneering were "starting to thunder," according to Joe. By this time, however, Ocean Systems was quietly slowing down. When Link left the organization, Joe turned his attention to Canada's underwater program.

In 1970 Joe was invited to Ottawa to help the Canadian government review its undersea activities—the country's marine science, ocean industry, ship-building and law of the sea. He completely immersed himself in Canada's sea program and, in 1973, his country announced a national ocean policy.

In 1969 he came up with the idea of *Sublimnos.*

"I thought that Canada should do something, maybe modest, but something," Joe said. "I decided that we could have a spartan underwater station by getting a few nickels and dimes together, open it up to everybody for use in scientific work. But mainly *Sublimnos* would be a catalyst to other bigger things."

To finance *Sublimnos,* Joe founded Undersea Research Ltd., a nonprofit center for research and education. The first significant funds came from the National Geographic Society. During the first winter Joe and his team worked in

Courtesy of Joe MacInnis

*1980: Discovery*

*Sublimnos,* they realized that the Great Lakes were very similar to the Arctic in terms of ice and other conditions.

"So I thought, 'Why not go to the big arena of the future?'" Joe said.

He assembled his first Arctic expedition in 1970, in which he and a team of four divers stayed 12 days and made 30 dives to see what could be explored in this frigid, polar world.

"All I wanted to do was look at the Arctic, look at the problems of equipment and human performance," Joe recalls. "We also did brief biological and geological surveys and tried to clarify the value of divers for that sort of operation."

The Arctic was, he saw, in many ways like the rest of the ocean 20 years before; and he saw that this region of the world would soon be explored for its resources:

> "You could descend through the Arctic interface and down through the water column to the bottom, and make a checklist. Oil and gas, pipelines, subsea production platforms, pollution and baseline studies, and the hundred-plus jobs that commercial divers do. They would eventually do them all in the Arctic: dock repair, salvage, tying in a completion system, whatever. My feeling was to get man up there on a nonurgent basis before a crisis arrived so that we could get some idea of what the problems were."

*1981: Dr. Joe MacInnis, Northwest Passage*

Courtesy of Joe MacInnis

Joe conducted a series of expeditions to the Arctic to give his team an insight into operating conditions during summer, winter, spring and fall. Each expedition grew larger in complexity, in people, in number of dives and in objectives. He began with four divers and stayed about a week. On the last trip he stayed nearly two months with 50 divers who made almost 300 dives.

*Sub–Igloo,* an offshoot of *Sublimnos,* was launched in 1972. The divers swam into *Sub–Igloo,* flushed out the inside water and peered out through a plexiglass sphere into the surrounding water. Although Carleton Ray had studied marine mammals from a habitat beneath the Antarctic ice in 1964, his habitat, *Sub–Ice Observation Chamber,* did not require divers to enter the frigid waters. *Sub–Ice* used a ladder that went down a tube from the surface so that the scientists never got wet.

Joe thought of his manned underwater project as a "virtual eyeball in the sea". The whole idea of *Sub–Igloo* was to build a "relatively low cost, highly portable, diver-buildable, transparent sphere." *Sub–Igloo* was placed at 35 feet in Resolute Bay, 600 miles north of the Arctic Circle. In his book *Underwater Man* Joe describes that first dive made in the cold, midnight-black waters.

It is time to go inside. I slip up through the hatch. My head breaks the surface. I remove my mask and hear the echo of my sigh. Cautiously I look around.

49

The water level is just below my chin, and I see small cakes of ice floating away on the wind of my steamy breath. The walls of *Sub–Igloo* seem not to exist.

I climb up on the bench and sit quietly. Three divers outside wave. One points beneath the bench. I lean over to look and see two small fish swimming there. I am in the Arctic's first undersea fishbowl. But the implications are larger than that.

The cold, clear water around me, so long the hidden home of arctic mammals and fish, is allowing us to probe its mysteries. This new tool, though, must be used with reverence. Yesterday an old Eskimo came into our tent, looked down the dive hole and said, "You will not scare our seals away, will you?" [1]

On December 13, 1972 Joe wrote me a letter from inside *Sub–Igloo*. "Hello and warm cheers from near the North Pole," the note began. On the envelope was the notice that the letter had been dispatched from the Arctic Ocean Floor at Resolute Bay. Still ahead for Joe was the North Pole.

In April, 1974 the Canadian Department of National Defense flew Joe and his team from Resolute Bay to Thule, and then to the military base at Alert Bay as part of a search and rescue rehearsal. From there, the divers were flown by helicopter 450 miles to the North Pole. "When we landed at the Pole, seven pararescue men parachuted out of one of the airplanes—some carrying Canadian flags . . . ," Joe said. "Some rehearsal! I was so moved by it all, that I cried. We made our camp and spent three days."

On April 28th, Joe and his team made the first North Pole dive.

"We were the first to dive and film under the top of the world. At the time, it was definitely the highlight of all the diving I'd ever done."

But every adventure Joe has ever undertaken is simply another step forward from his previous work. Following his early Arctic explorations, he produced a television series for CBC called "The New Wave," ten programs in which cameras focused on "the entire gamut from ocean energy to the Great Lakes."

During this time, he continued to write. "Writing," he said, "is the fountainhead of all clear thought." Today, he is still writing and, at this point, working on a novel.

Joe took a break in 1976 to study and teach. That year he took his family to Cambridge, England, where he studied and lectured at the Scott Polar Research Institute.

Then followed the complicated series of expeditions to find and document HMS *Breadalbane*, a 19th-century British barque which sank in 1853 off Beechey Island in the Northwest Passage. The shipwreck, located 600 miles north of the

*Courtesy of Joe MacInnis*

*1983: Dr. Joe MacInnis prepares to spend a day in the freezing temperatures of the Artic.*

Arctic circle, was the northernmost shipwreck ever discovered on the sea floor. For years, *Breadalbane*'s gravesite remained impenetrable because of unusually heavy summer ice.

During these frustrating years, Joe occasionally sent letters to me about his disappointments. On November 22, 1979 he announced: "Another frustrating year in our search for HMS *Breadalbane*—whose bones still lie under the gloomy guardians of ice."

On April 16, 1981: "It's been a splendid year with the discovery of the HMS *Breadbox*. However, there was a bump in the road when we looked at the ice conditions and decided not to go this year. About 48 hours of depression and gnashing of teeth cured that. Next year for sure."

On May 20, 1982: "I've just come back from the high Arctic and a look at the ice over the *Breadalbane*. It was a fascinating trip that confirmed the reasons for postponing this year and also sparked an idea for solving the problem next year. . . . Instead of a D-8 Cat Train across the ice, we'll get a pair of Hercules, each carrying 40,000 pounds of gear, to fly it directly into the site. We're going to cut out an airstrip on the flat near-shore ice in Erebus Bay."

The next news I had of Joe and *Breadalbane* was with the July 1983 issue of *National Geographic.* On the magazine cover is a photo of a diver being lowered through a hole in the ice in a *Wasp* submersible. (*Wasp,* developed by engineer/ designer Graham Hawkes, is a cross between a one-man submarine and a diving suit that allows a diver to go deep while remaining at surface pressure.) Inside the *National Geographic* report was a preview of the dives made on the *Breadalbane* by Joe and his team during 18 days in May, 1983.

That is the way with Joe—never giving up, despite the freezing odds. In 1986 he wrote that he had been working as a writer and consultant with Robert Ballard on the discovery of the *Titanic,* and had been involved with Mel Fisher's *Atocha* adventure as well.

In the meantime, he was travelling and lecturing all over the world. Currently he is planning another big Arctic project.

Joe's achievements are inspirational. Many of his difficult expeditions were accomplished on shoestring budgets. He said, "I never go for big dollar support. I don't believe that one should ask for it. I don't believe that one should go to Washington or Ottawa with a big tin cup in his hands. I think that if you have a viable idea with national implications, the first thing to do is see if it will stand on its own merit. We went to industry and we went to institutions and that's where we got the money. We didn't need or want much. In fact, we haven't had any government money for any of the Arctic expeditions except the last one. But we got a lot of other support in terms of aircraft and equipment. I don't believe in the welfare state. Man must be productive if he is to remain free."

## Notes

1.  Joe MacInnis, *Underwater Man* (McClelland and Stewart, Ltd.: Toronto, 1974), pp. 141–142.

## Suggested Reading

Joe MacInnis, *Underwater Man* (McClelland and Stewart, Ltd.: Toronto, 1974).
Joseph B. MacInnis, ``Diving Beneath Arctic Ice'' (*National Geographic Magazine*, August 1973).
Joseph B. MacInnis, ``Exploring a 140-Year-Old Ship Under Arctic Ice'' (*National Geographic Magazine*, July 1983).

## Chapter 6

*Jacques Cousteau*

# Jacques Cousteau:
# The Mystique and the Magic

*O we can wait no longer,*
*We too take ship O soul,*
*Joyous we too launch out on*
*trackless seas,*
*Fearless for unknown shores.*


— *Walt Whitman*

I swam across the rocks and compared myself favorably with the sars. To swim fishlike, horizontally, was the logical method in a medium 800 times denser than air. To halt and hang attached to nothing, no lines or air pipe to the surface, was a dream. At night I often had visions of flying by extending my arms as wings. Now I flew without wings.[1]

It was late June, 1943 and Jacques Yves Cousteau was making his first scuba dive with a revolutionary breathing device he had developed with the French engineer Emile Gagnan. Captain Cousteau, a French navy gunnery officer, was dissatisfied with man's superficial probing of the ocean surface. It was not enough that man could stay and look as long as he could hold his breath. Cousteau felt that the gas-flow demand regulators (which had already been designed by Gagnan for use on automobiles and in hospital operating rooms during World War II) could be modified for use underwater. Gagnan and Cousteau tried several concepts and finally came up with a successful model of an open-circuit, compressed-air scuba.

Cousteau's vision and foresight created a long-awaited pathway to the ocean depths. He, in turn, realized his dream of flying underwater and swimming like a fish. More importantly, with the practical help of Gagnan, Cousteau enabled man to look inside the ocean and study its innermost secrets.

In the years since the inception of the Aqualung, Cousteau's name has become synonymous with ocean exploration. He has led numerous teams of divers to explore, examine and investigate many facets of the submarine world. As man extended his frontier deeper and wider beneath the water interface, Cousteau produced films and books about the beauty of the underwater world. Because of him, thousands of landlocked people have seen the ocean wave and learned about sea life from whales to octopus.

In 1969 while Dick and I were in Europe researching the Hannes Keller story, we made a side trip to Monaco. To this day I remember the awe in which we walked along Monaco's romantic cliffside paths, looking down at the glittery casinos, expensive hotels and restaurants that lined a yacht-filled bay. We passed the stately palace of Prince Rainier and his fairy-tale princess, Grace Kelly. As we looked up at the lighted windows, we could only imagine what their royal life was like.

Then we arrived at the cliffside Oceanographic Institute and Museum where Cousteau was appointed director in 1957. Its white walls shined in the moonlight; the sea crashed on the cliffs below. The entire setting was like a scene out of a Dumas novel.

We returned to the museum the next day and spoke with an official who took us through the building, established by Prince Albert, Rainier's grandfather, as an oceanographic museum. We saw how Cousteau had taken Albert's dreams of a great marine laboratory, dusted them off and revitalized them. In one of the high-ceilinged rooms was Albert's collection of huge sea mammal skeletons: a stuffed squid about 40 feet long, Albert's whaleboat, ancient oceanographic instruments and mannequins of early scientists in the midst of their work. In another hall was an exhibit of modern oceanography, complete with a bathyscaph and a full-scale model of Cousteau's new diving saucer.

What I remember most about the museum, however, is Cousteau's father's bicycle—one of the old ones with an enormous wheel in front and a small wheel in back. We took it outside and took pictures of ourselves sitting on it.

At the time, Cousteau was on an expedition aboard the *Calypso,* the converted minesweeper that had become the most famed research vessel in the world. Cousteau's first expedition aboard the ship was in 1951, when his crew sailed it from its home port in Toulon to the Red Sea. Here, Cousteau and his team had made diving excursions to document the coral reef life. In 1951 this was still an extraordinary view of the planet. The expedition had resulted in Cousteau's first *National Geographic* article, filled with photographs taken by underwater cameras developed by Cousteau. From these beginnings evolved

*Research vessel Calypso on location during a Mississippi River filming expedition conducted by the Cousteau Society.*

both the immensely successful book, *The Silent World*, which described Cousteau's early explorations, and the film documentaries that captivated the world.

I was six years old at the time *The Silent World* was published. I remember my mother telling my brother, sister and me what a monumental thing it was that a man should discover life in the sea where no one had ever looked before. She said it showed how much more man can always learn just when he thinks he knows everything. A fan of Greek myths, she also loved the fact that *Calypso* was named for the daughter of Atlas and Tethys, who in Homer's *Odyssey* detains the shipwrecked Odysseus on her island for seven years, promising him immortality.

I grew up on early Cousteau films. I remember one old black-and-white epic wherein Cousteau and his divers are exploring an ancient shipwreck. In the dialogue a tremulous narrator announced the fact that if the men were to surface too fast, their "heads would explode like a rotten melon." That was pretty dramatic stuff, though it seems funny now. One must remember, however, that Cousteau began his early explorations in the 1930s, years before anyone knew the effects of deep-diving for too long.

Born June 11, 1910 in Saint-Andre-de Cubzac, Cousteau began his diving experiments when he was 26, breathing through garden hoses and masks fashioned from inner tubes. His diving partners in those days were Philippe Tailliez, a lieutenant Cousteau met during World War I, and a beach-loving artist named Frederic Dumas.

Cousteau, assigned to navy artillery, ammunitions and gunnery equipment in Toulon, had suffered serious, almost fatal, injuries in a car accident and one arm remained severely damaged. He was told by Tailliez that he could strengthen his arm by swimming. Cousteau took the advice and stayed with it. Together the three friends began to explore the underwater world, making their first subsea forays with homemade equipment, determined to find ways to stay below the surface for longer periods of time. They experimented with oxygen tanks, which nearly killed them since oxygen below 30 feet is toxic. Cousteau also began his first attempts at underwater photography, designing a waterproof housing for his Beaulieu camera. His first images were of Dumas spearfishing.

In 1937 Cousteau married Simone Melchior, a woman who loved the sea and who helped him in his early diving experiments. Later when *Calypso* became a world travelling expedition center, Simone accompanied her husband and his team on every trip, pulling the men together, solving shipboard problems and keeping together a tight *esprit de corps*. In 1938 their son, Jean-Michel, was born in Toulon, a strategic port where Cousteau served in a defense station as the war escalated in Europe. Two years later Simone gave birth to their second son, Philippe, named after Tailliez.

During the European conflict, Cousteau continued his underwater experiments. At one point, he approached father-in-law "Daddy" Melchior for help in producing an underwater breathing device. Cousteau needed to devise a method that would enable a diver to inhale and exhale, through the same mouthpiece, without breathing back in the carbon dioxide that is emitted during exhalation. Underwater, excessive carbon dioxide can cause "shallow-water blackout", or a loss of consciousness.

Melchior, an executive with a French company that made oxygen, nitrogen, carbon dioxide and other gases, was willing to help. He led Cousteau to Air Liquide engineer Emile Gagnan, who had in his laboratory just the device Cousteau was looking for—an automatic shutoff valve designed for use on automobiles that were running on natural gas.

In three weeks, Cousteau and Gagnan produced a prototype of an Aqualung and, in the early spring of 1943, Cousteau made his first dive in a river outside Paris. The dive was not completely successful, because air continually escaped from the makeshift regulator. But Cousteau pressed on. By summer he had an Aqualung that would allow him to swim freely, and he experimented with flips, rolls and deeper dives. Cousteau, Dumas and Tailliez spent many months trying the new invention at greater depths and in different realms of underwater exploration. They discovered the drunken "raptures of the deep" caused by a buildup of nitrogen in the body when the diver descends below 100 feet, and they learned about the "bends". They found that when a diver surfaces too rapidly, or ascends while holding his breath, he could suffer an air embolism, wherein air bubbles leak into the bloodstream and lodge in the brain or other body parts.

Air Liquide formed a subsidiary, Spirotechnique, which began manufacturing regulators and air tanks. These units were eventually named SCUBA (self-contained underwater breathing apparatus). Cousteau convinced the military that the equipment could be used in underwater wartime maneuvers; and it wasn't long before Spirotechnique was sending scuba units overseas to Rene Bussoz through his company, U.S. Divers.

Dick worked for U.S. Divers during those days, and recalls the astonishing announcement—"The market is flooded"—which came after 20 units had been shipped from France to the U.S. Of course, it came to pass that scuba equipment would eventually be used by hundreds of thousands of divers worldwide.

Cousteau's interest in the underwater world extended far beyond recreational swimming just below the surface of the sea. In the early 1960s he began to experiment with ways to put men underwater for extended periods of time, so that they could be residents of the sea, rather than mere visitors. He even envisioned men breathing water, a concept which had some scientists raising

*Captain and crew discuss the day's work (right). Below, Cousteau and divers examine a specimen from the river.*

*Whether aboard ship (opposite) or on land, each day of an expedition provides action and discovery.*

Courtesy of Cousteau Society

Courtesy of Cousteau Society

their eyebrows. Cousteau, however, was not worried about what others thought of his ideas. If that had been the case, he might never have pursued the invention of the Aqualung.

In 1962 the concept of underwater man was being explored on several fronts. Florida diving pioneer Ed Link was launching the first phase of his Man-in-Sea program. About the same time, Cousteau began his Conshelf (short for Continental Shelf Station) experiments. In September 1962 two divers lived for a week at 36 feet in the Mediterranean in a capsule called *Diogenes*. Cousteau reported this success at the World Congress on Underwater Activities as an example of how diving was going beyond recreation into a new way of life.

Conshelf II took place the following year. This time, five divers stayed at 36 feet in the Red Sea, in an underwater home called the *Starfish House*. The divers came and went from the underwater habitat, usually for exploratory dives in the immediate vicinity of the submerged home. On several occasions, some of the divers made short plunges from the habitat to depths of over 300 feet. Cousteau himself lived for four days in the *Starfish House*. Other divers, including Simone, paid short visits from the surface. Out of this experiment came the film, "World Without Sun."

In 1965 Cousteau launched Conshelf III by placing a habitat at 300 feet in the Mediterranean. Here six divers, including Philippe Cousteau and expedition leader Andre Laban, stayed 30 days, making daily dives to almost 400 feet while breathing heliox, a mixture of helium and oxygen. While in the habitat, Philippe Cousteau and Laban talked by transcontinental telephone to aquanaut/astronaut Scott Carpenter, who was 200 feet below the Pacific Ocean off Southern California in the U.S. Navy's *Sealab II*.

The Conshelf dives were among the last of Cousteau's experiments in extended underwater living. From here he turned his attention to filmmaking expeditions that brought to the public an understandable view of the undersea world. Although "pure" researchers sometimes scoff at popularized "show-biz science," Cousteau took the view that much scientific research is lost on the public, shielded in technological language and hidden away in libraries. He meant to let the average citizen know what goes on in the depths of the ocean. He also spread the message that the seas of the planet need to be protected from increasing encroachments of man-made pollution.

My introduction to Cousteau came in early 1973, when Paul Tzimoulis, publisher of *Skin Diver Magazine*, asked me to interview the famous French captain. Cousteau had just formed the Cousteau Society, an organization designed to work for and in the oceans of the world. Cousteau had turned from ocean exploration to ocean conservation. His explorations focused on marine environments that now needed protection.

As I think of it now, I am in awe of the short span of time it took the unknown world of the sea to become overknown and exploited. Cousteau sensed the tide and the need for this realization and was now fully dedicated to informing the world about the ocean's plight. He was producing educational films of adventure and beauty, and didn't hesitate to emphasize his views in strong narrations. He said the oceans which had opened the doors to his own adventures and discoveries were now in need of help.

I found Cousteau to be as I expected, dynamic and wonderfully weathered by the oceans. As we discussed the sea, he became animated, punctuating his thoughts with his hands. When he spoke of the crimes against the earth's water system, he became impassioned. His theme: If we don't care enough about the seas of the world, we don't care enough about ourselves.

"We know that the cycle of life in general is identical to the cycle of water," he said. "Because of that, just fighting for the ocean is not enough. First, we have to fight for the entire water system, not only the ocean. There is but one water system—the ocean is the biggest part of it, but there is only one system. And because that water system dramatically conditions the way we live, it follows that fighting for the water system is also fighting for the quality of our lives."

The Society, Cousteau said, had taken up the fight. "What we are doing is protecting and improving life, including human life, of course—that being our greatest concern. But the life of other animals is conditioning human life, so we have to get into that. We are not conservationists for the sake of conservation. We are conservationists because it has an influence on the quality of our lives. We are centered on man; but we now know very clearly that we cannot disassociate any living entity from the ocean, from the water system, from the life cycle."

I think of how prophetic were these words spoken over a dozen years ago. As government officials now argue about the pros and cons of dumping nuclear wastes at sea, and as more and more enclosed bays and estuaries become off limits to the harvesting of shellfish because of pollution, one cannot help but wonder how these problems might have been solved earlier had we listened to Cousteau. Some scientists scoffed at his words, saying his warning signals were alarmist tactics, but Cousteau continued with his message anyway. In the year following our interview, the Cousteau Society, in cooperation with Goddard Space Flight Center and Texas A&M University, organized a study of the conflicting forces in the ocean: the productivity of life versus man-made lethal pollution. Instruments were installed on the *Calypso* to measure oceanographic features, such as the chemical content of sea water, temperature, depth factors, water colors, kinds and quantities of pollutants present. Two cruises were organized along the western coast of Florida and in the "plume" of the Mississippi River.

In 1975 Cousteau testified before the California Assembly Resources and Land Use Committee, recommending a fight against ignorance of the problems of the sea and advocating a relief from the pressures of coastline population. He proposed to fight pollution by prevention rather than researching a cure. He asked for a ban on spearfishing, as well as on the trading of coral and seashells.

Cousteau participated in national energy conferences, attacking the "cost benefit" theory of damage assessment. Pointing to the 1969 Santa Barbara oil spill, he said, "Every single damage was evaluated in dollars and cents, to prove that the benefits from careless offshore drilling outweighed the costs of the accident. But the nonsense of the system, when pushed to the extreme, exploded when it came to putting a price tag on life: How much is the cost of a bird? One dollar! One dollar is the price poachers get for a squirrel! How much for an extinct species? How much for the blue whale? Are we going to put a price tag on my three-year-old granddaughter? What savings would justify the sacrifice of future generations?"

Cousteau began to sound an alarm on an international level, too. He participated in International Law-of-the-Sea conferences, summarizing his declaration that the ocean resources should be the common property of all mankind. He stressed the need for remote sensing and mass telemetry from satellites and aircraft as investigative methods to survey the health of the ocean. A permanent global remote sensing system, he said, could monitor productivity and pollution from thousands of instrumented buoys, drifting or anchored, in the oceans of the world.

"This is the only way for man to sense the pulse of the oceans," Cousteau said.

To augment his personal campaign about the plight of the sea, the Cousteau Society launched its television series, *Oasis in Space,* in which cameras focused on earth, oceans, forests and life, and on the technology that is guiding the world into its future. He produced *The Water Planet,* a series of filmstrips for junior high and high schools. Other films included the environmental insights of prominent thinkers, such as Paul Ehrlich, Margaret Mead, Carl Sagan, Buckminster Fuller and Isaac Asimov.

The Cousteau Society began its "Involvement Day" gatherings around the U.S., where thousands of people participated in workshops led by prominent speakers, such as Dr. Wesley Marx, author of *The Frail Ocean,* and ocean biochemist Dr. Rim Fay, who more recently sounded an alarm about the pollution of the Santa Monica Bay in California.

JACQUES COUSTEAU: THE MYSTIQUE AND THE MAGIC

As I wrote about my interview with Cousteau, I reflected on how much understanding of the ocean he has given the world. Anyone who has seen a Cousteau film, whether it is about an octopus or the entire Amazon basin, cannot help but be affected by the life cycles he focuses his cameras on. Because of him, millions of people have watched red salmon migrate upstream, and they've seen manatees digging for food in the sandy beds of their inshore habitats of Florida. Cousteau has turned more people on to the sea than anyone else in the world. And he continues his outreach to the public with a strong hand, producing films, publishing books and creating ocean centers where people can see for themselves the wonders of the sea.

Whether or not the layman or scientist agrees with his views, there are few who don't appreciate what Cousteau has contributed. This appreciation shows in a profound admiration that follows him wherever he goes. The ubiquitous red cap and sharp-nosed profile are familiar to the average citizen of the world. My friend Jack McKenney, who worked as a cameraman in the Falkland Islands as part of the Cousteau series, *Rediscovery of the World,* described how the public reacted when they saw the famous French captain in an airport.

"It was unbelievable," McKenney said. "They'd rush up to him in complete awe. They would interrupt him to ask for everything from autographs to information about snorkels."

Although public adulation might be a nuisance, no amount of appreciation could be enough for a man who has devoted his life to making the sea accessible to so many people.

### Notes

1. Jacques Cousteau, *The Silent World* (Harper & Brothers Publishers: New York, 1953), p. 6.

### Suggested Reading

Jacques Cousteau, *The Silent World* (Harper & Brothers Publishers: New York, 1953).
Jacques Cousteau, *World Without Sun* (Harper & Row: New York, 1965).
Jacques Cousteau, *The Shark: Splendid Savage of the Sea* (Doubleday & Company, Inc.: New York, 1970).
Philippe Diole, *The Undersea Adventure* (Julian Messner, Inc.: New York, 1953).
Wesley Marx, *The Frail Ocean* (Coward-McCann, Inc.: New York, 1967).

## Chapter 7

*The Alcyone*

# Sons of Cousteau:
# Carrying On in the Wake

*Ride on! Rough-shod if need be,*
*smooth-shod if that will do,*
*but ride on!*
*Ride on over all obstacles*
*and win the race!*


— *Dickens*

---

I met Philippe Cousteau in Chicago at a diving convention where he was on the evening film program as an honored guest. I was on in the afternoon talking about fishes; he was talking about the world. After we were introduced, we began to talk about Paris. I told him about the time I had witnessed the flight of a paper airplane from the Eiffel Tower and how wild the Parisians had been. They had cheered, stomped and roared as they watched the plane soar for miles and miles until it disappeared over the Seine.

Philippe listened carefully, then made his comment. "It's the *Tour Eefell*," he said.

I didn't know what to say. While I stood there figuring out the next thing to do, he suddenly roared with laughter. Philippe could make a person feal uneasy in one minute, but wonderful the next. It was all commensurate with his capricious moods. In later years I saw him sophisticated and deeply serious with one person, then outrageously prankish with another only minutes later. Through all of his moments of mirth, however, one had the feeling that beneath the joyful surface of Philippe Cousteau was that sober, resolute outlook: humor with purpose.

Philippe was a backbone of the Cousteau Society films, leading *Calypso* expeditions anywhere from the frozen Antarctica to the Blue Holes of the Bahamas. He always wore a red woven cap, insignia of the Cousteau mystique. He filmed the beavers of Canada, whales of Patagonia, dolphins, dugongs and

*Jacques Cousteau*

Courtesy of Cousteau Society

sharks. Although he walked in a path carved by his father, he held his own aura. For a good while it irked him to always, *always* be introduced as the "son of Jacques Cousteau".

"Aren't I my own person?" he whispered to me after his Chicago introduction. Later it ceased to bother him. After all, it was a fact of life.

Philippe was an avid flyer, and flying proved to be his nemesis. In 1977, during an expedition to Easter Island, he crashed in a gyrocopter and miraculously survived. However, his right leg was badly broken, his kneecap shattered into tiny fragments. There was speculation that he'd never walk normally again. Philippe's serious and purposeful nature took the reins of the situation, and he began a long, arduous program of physical therapy in Monaco. Dr. Joe MacInnis, the Canadian doctor of underwater medicine, went to see Philippe in Monaco. Philippe described his therapy to Joe as the "Spanish Inquisition".

Because of the nature of his work, MacInnis had been on hand during many of the tragedies and afflictions of fallen explorers, and he developed a special ability to comfort those who suffered damage or loss. He wrote about Philippe during this time: "Each morning before breakfast, he disappeared out the door to that silent inner place where thin muscles fight pulleys and weights, where tight ligaments struggle against pain, where drops of sweat grow like storm clouds on the forehead. He would return around noon looking pale and worn."

Joe asked Philippe, gently, if he thought he might regain the use of his leg, and Philippe had said, "I'll win this round—and be flying and diving again—no matter how long it takes."

The two friends met later in Los Angeles. As they discussed their careers, Philippe confessed, "Eventually I would like to move away from the ocean and make films that grapple with the larger imponderables of life: love, war, loneliness and death—at least for a while. When I come back to the sea, I would have new strengths, new insights."

On June 28, 1979, Philippe Cousteau was landing a PBY amphibious airplane in a river near Lisbon, Portugal. Suddenly a hatch in the nose section of the plane opened up, caught the surface of the water and caused the plane to crash. Philippe was killed instantly. It was a tragedy too horrible for anyone to imagine.

A few months after the accident I saw Jacques Cousteau at a memorial concert given for Philippe at an outdoor arena in Ventura, California. When I arrived backstage I saw him at the microphone, holding the audience in rapt attention. Rapter, even, than Crosby, Stills and Nash who had just preceded him. I looked at the familiar profile from where I stood, the bright lights shining on his white head, and I marveled at the mystique he held for people all over the world. He had captured their imaginations, helped them to understand the sea, inspired their love of adventure and of nature.

Then he came down from the stage and the audience exploded in applause. I reached out to him and told him how badly I felt about Philippe, how much I had admired him, how much we would all miss him.

As long as I live I will never forget his face at that moment. "Yes," he said, "it is terrible. It is terrible." He wanted to talk about it and he didn't want to talk about it. He wanted it to go away, but the grief was etched deeply into his face. His beloved son was gone. There was no way to get him back.

Today, when I see some of the early Cousteau films, with Philippe vital and alive—diving, flying and doing adventurous things—I can still hear his father's voice saying, "It is terrible. It is terrible."

I didn't get to know Jean-Michel Cousteau until years later when we were both at a diving convention in San Antonio, Texas. Although we'd met before, all I knew of Jean-Michel was that he loved his work as a marine architect. He didn't care for the cinematic limelight or administrative desk work that is part of running an empire as far-reaching as the Cousteau Society. Basically, he stayed aloof from the films and the publicity, working out concepts for the construction of underwater wildlife reserves for exotic islands such as Wuvulu, a tiny coral atoll in the Bismarck Archipelago near New Guinea.

Now, with Philippe gone, Jean-Michel had no choice but to step into position within the Society. Soon he, too, was diving and exploring far-off regions, such as the Amazon Basin.

In San Antonio, I'd been asked to do an on-camera, impromptu interview with Jean-Michel. I readily agreed. While the cameras rolled we began seriously, but within five minutes, seriousness went out the window. We hammed it up, clowning and talking about everything but diving.

Then, in 1986, when I was assigned by the *Santa Barbara News–Press* to cover the arrival of the Cousteau windship *Alcyone* at Santa Barbara Harbor, I leaped at the chance to see Jean-Michel again. *Alcyone,* a unique, twin-stacked ship, was exploring the islands on the other side of the Santa Barbara Channel: the San Miguel, Santa Rosa, Santa Cruz, Anacapa and Santa Barbara islands, and further south, Catalina, San Nicolas, and San Clemente.

The California islands were the last leg of the travels of *Alcyone* to the islands of the Pacific coast from Vancouver to Mexico. The film of *Alcyone*'s adventures were to be part of the Cousteau television series, *Rediscovery of the World.* The captain, Philippe Rueff, had programmed the ship's navigational computer so it would arrive in Santa Barbara on a midweek day, at exactly 10 a.m.

As I thought about my assignment, I thought I'd do one better: I would arrange to ride aboard *Alcyone* from Ventura to Santa Barbara, and I'd talk to Jean-Michel on the way up the coast. I called the Cousteau Society office in Los Angeles, and the staff made arrangements for me.

I don't know who said "time waits for no one," but that is exactly the truth. On the morning of my intended sail I was horrified to discover that I had overslept! I leaped into my car with my shoes untied and sped down the freeway, hoping to make the 30-mile trip from Santa Barbara south to Ventura in about 20 minutes.

As I reached the Ventura area, I was pulled over by a policeman for speeding. As I imagined the twin stacks of the windship pulling out of the Ventura Harbor, I begged the policeman to let me go, but to no avail. I regained an appreciation of speed limits: driving beyond them is both unhealthy and illegal.

When I got to the Ventura Harbor, I was just in time to see *Alcyone*'s stacks glide by the breakwater. I ran down to a marina next to Channel Islands National Park headquarters, and sauntering up one of the docks was Joe, captain of the charter boat *Kingfish.*

"Help, help," I said. "Can you run me in a boat to that ship just going out of the harbor?"

There was a rapid exchange of money for fuel. In about two minutes, Joe and I were speeding in a fairly fast launch toward the wake of the Cousteau windship. Except we weren't fast enough. As *Alcyone* passed the breakwater, it began a wide

# SONS OF COUSTEAU:    CARRYING ON IN THE WAKE

*Jean-Michel  Cousteau*

*Philippe  Cousteau*

*Courtesy of Cousteau Society*

Jean-Michel climbing out of a
submersible

turn up the coast. The two 33-foot-tall cylindrical aluminum sails turned toward the wind. Thus began the aeronautical magic that swept the ship from our grasp.

*Alcyone,* named for the daughter of Aeolus, Greek god of the winds, was proving her mettle. It was a warm day, with breezes just enough to work the giant wind stacks that propel the ship. The stacks of *Alcyone* are actually two "aspirated" wind cylinders that propel the 109-foot vessel at speeds of a conventional sailing vessel. The cylinders work on a nineteenth-century theory known as the "Magnus effect". The "effect," named for the German chemist Heinrich Gustav Magnus, is essentially that a lift arises from the lateral force of an air current on a cylinder. Moveable shutters exposed to the wind, together with a fan which sucks wind through the vents into the cylinder, provide lift and propulsion for the boat. The wind-propulsion design cuts fuel consumption by 30 to 40 percent.

From our little launch, I admired the unusual look of the ship—flat and wide, with two tall cylinders.

"We'll never catch her now," Joe said.

Thinking fast, he took a sharp starboard turn toward a commercial fishing vessel lumbering out of the harbor alongside us. This was the good ship *Garibaldi.* The *Garibaldi* is bright orange, like the California ocean goldfish that

72

bears the same name. It is the workboat of the Garibaldi Commercial Fishing and Diving Co. of Ventura, which will unsnag a propeller or catch you a few fish.

Aboard the *Garibaldi* were three gillnetters, partners for the past three years—Jay and Frank Kemsley and Bob Love. They agreed immediately to take me aboard. They throttled the *Garibaldi* up the coast toward *Alcyone.*

Sometimes it appeared we would catch the ship, but other times it seemed like a lost cause. Jay went to the radio and called the windship. A French voice came over the radio. It was Captain Philippe Rueff. Jay told him he had a reporter on the *Garibaldi* who was trying to catch up with him. Rueff said *Alcyone* was on a computerized course and could not slow down. (Later, Rueff said he thought some mad photographer was trying to get a picture of the boat.)

Jay steered the *Garibaldi* toward a fast-moving lobster fishing boat working in the area. The lobster fishermen said they were worried about getting their traps up before the winds hit. By now, we were about three miles out of Ventura Harbor. I realized I hadn't thought of what I would do if I ended up in the position I was now in.

"Looks like you're going fishing with us," said Jay. "Are you good at pulling in nets?"

They wouldn't be finished until about noon or 1 o'clock, they said. I couldn't answer. *Alcyone* would pull into the Santa Barbara Harbor at 10 a.m., and I would fail to get the story because I wouldn't be there.

The three gillnetters got into their slickers and were soon hooking the line of their first net. The catch was kingfish, a type of croaker. The *Garibaldi* boys said they'd sell the kingfish to a buyer in San Pedro. On this day they planned to bring in 1,000 pounds.

I watched as they removed each fish by hand. They explained how the gills of the fish reveal its freshness: red gills mean the fish is good, black gills mean they've been in the nets too long. A sailboat came by, but not close enough. Jay held up a clear, gooey teardrop-shaped blob, which hung on a piece of kelp.

"Squid eggs," he announced.

A spider crab hit the deck. Bob picked it up and threw it overboard. About this time, a massive gray boat appeared on the horizon. It was moving fast in our direction.

"Fish and Game," Jay said.

"They'll probably get you for $500, for being on a commercial boat without a license," Bob said.

"I don't care, call them over here," I said.

The boat was the *Albacore,* a fast-moving patrol vessel used by state Fish and Game Department wardens. Jay left the net and went to the marine radio. He told the captain of the *Albacore* that he had a reporter stranded on board. The *Albacore* agreed to come over and check us out as soon as it went to the aid of the lobster fishermen we had talked to previously. They were now dead in the water.

When the *Albacore* came around, the captain, Gene Martin, exploded with laughter. What was I doing aboard the *Garibaldi,* he wanted to know. He said he'd take me back to the Ventura Harbor, which he did at 22 knots. I was back at the dock within half an hour.

On the freeway I spotted the happy officer. He was now writing up some other speeder. I beeped and waved at him as I drove by. He looked up and waved back.

It was exactly 10 a.m. when I arrived at the Santa Barbara Harbor. The *Alcyone* was waiting to pull up to the Navy Pier—on time and ready to face the crowds of people who had gathered to greet the ship.

Jean-Michel, standing near the forward wind stack, saw me and gave me a scolding sign. Later aboard *Alcyone,* I told Jean-Michel and the others my story—about Joe in the skiff, the gillnetters aboard the *Garibaldi,* the kingfish with their black gills and red gills, the Fish and Game rescue and the happy cop writing out tickets.

Jean-Michel said, "Forget our trip. That's the story; write it."

Later that afternoon, Jean-Michel and I sat on the beach, and he talked about his ideas and some upcoming projects. He was about to leave for Washington, D.C. to meet with NASA officials about some documentaries he and his father had in mind. Satellites would enable a filmed communication between Jean-Michel and his father, who was working aboard the *Calypso* in the South Pacific.

"The perspective of space is important in considering the planet," Jean-Michel said. "If we can pull away from the planet, we can see the planet—that it's not a bad place to stay."

He remembered receiving news of the Challenger space shuttle disaster. At the time, he was filming on a mountaintop at the tip of Cape Horn. "There were people there of all nations," he said. "We all cried together. There were no barriers."

Unity of mankind was to be one of the themes of a new Cousteau project in Paris—the Cousteau Ocean Center. He envisioned the center as a space and underwater park. It would be one of his pet projects—a compilation of ideas architectural, biological and philosophical.

He envisioned a moving walkway that would take visitors inside a teardrop where a mime act would point out that humans are 75 percent water. In an outer-space exhibit one could see that the Earth is a water planet. In another, people could travel inside a whale, going first into the mouth, over the tongue, and then into the heart, blubber and body of the animal.

The ideas continued, and Jean-Michel said that although his father had been asked if his television series *Rediscovery of the World* was to be his last major film effort, the question was "completely stupid". Films, like ideas, flow nonstop in minds that never cease to explore. When I saw Jean-Michel some months later in Ventura, he said the Cousteau films continue to evolve both philosophically and creatively.

"Look at the old Cousteau films," he said. "They took one subject—a whale, sea otter—just one species, and then dissected it all ways. We've grown out of that. We've evolved from looking at a species to looking at the problems surrounding it. That's where we are now—how do humans relate to the environment, to planet Earth? Not to point fingers, but to make better choices."

Jean-Michel said his adventures are born of the need to get this message across to his "fellow humans". Sometimes he doesn't particularly enjoy the physical exhaustion that comes from what he undertakes, but he goes forward anyway. He talked about climbing Mount Mismi, 18,000 feet up in the Peruvian Andes, as part of the Cousteau television documentary on the Amazon. The hike was exhausting by day, and it was so cold at night, the men huddled together in their tents to get warm. The documentary team's goal was to get to the head of the Amazon River and work their way down the 4,000-mile stream to the Atlantic Ocean. The expedition took three months.

"Morally I was O.K., because I was a leader," Jean-Michel said. "If I hadn't been a leader, I might have quit. It was painful."

Because the responsibility was on his back, he was willing to undertake the difficult. But also he said that adventure is a "way to go out and see for myself—a motivation."

"Only people who don't do anything don't make mistakes. That's one of my favorite sayings. Adventure is what helps you wake up in the morning."

## Chapter 8

*Ron and Valerie Taylor*

# Ron and Valerie Taylor:
# Cavorting with Sharks

*Our interest's
in the dangerous edge
of things.*


— *Browning*


In October, 1980 my friend Annie Doubilet and I swam at 80 feet along Desco Reef in the clear blue water of the Coral Sea. We could see the white sand bottom below us at 130 feet as we hugged the vertical wall of the drop-off. We inspected the purple corals, the multicolored tropical fishes and the bright little nudibranchs. We were as happy as could be.

Out of nowhere a grey reef shark zoomed in and buzzed us. It swam off into the distance, then turned sharply and came back. Then from the original direction it had come, three more sharks swam in, and all of them began to circle over the open sandy bottom just off the reef. We began to back up—both of us trying awfully hard to make ourselves small.

Before we knew it five sharks, the biggest one about five-and-a-half feet long, were circling and watching us, never going too far out of view. Then a little one, about three feet long, came up from behind in a surprise approach. With this the other sharks began to behave as if a fish had been speared somewhere, swimming erratically in ever tighter circles. As the big one came in for a close pass, we saw mating scars etched all over its back.

By this time our own backs were against the reef and we were trying not to breathe. The sharks continued to circle. We knew that reef sharks are not considered to be man-eating or necessarily all that dangerous, but among

77

sharks, they are the little nippers with nasty tempers. Like all sharks, they have teeth.

Suddenly the big one turned, came straight as a torpedo at us and didn't veer off until it was just two feet away. We were being dive-bombed!

I signalled to Annie that I had had enough and wanted to clear out. Together we swam up and over the reef wall, into a shallow area that was protected by a number of huge coral heads. Just as we got into the quiet of this subsea lagoon, we bumped smack into an enormous nurse shark, which Annie later guessed to be 12 to 13 feet long. I guessed it to be more like 100 feet long. It was so big it looked like a submarine. I almost swallowed my regulator when I saw it.

We turned to get around the nurse shark, which was never any threat because these sluggish animals just lumber along minding their own business. No sooner had we cleared the shark than we bumped into a sea snake wriggling its way to the surface. Sea snakes are common in the Coral Sea and are said to be docile creatures with gentle natures. However, if one happens to bite you by accident, its venom is more deadly than a cobra's. Annie and I decided then and there to swim back to the boat and call it a day.

Valerie Taylor, fearless shark star of Australia, laughed like mad when she heard our story. Somewhere on the same reef she and her husband Ron had been chumming the waters to get the sharks into a feeding frenzy for a film they were shooting. At the same time, David, Annie's husband, had been chumming the water elsewhere on the same reef because he was photographing frenzied sharks for a *National Geographic* story. The sharks we had seen, said Valerie, were swimming back and forth between the two feeding frenzies, alternating between banquets, and we were just meeting them in the middle. Valerie laughed all over again at the very thought of it.

I was in Australia for a second time, and on assignment for *National Geographic*. My story was not on sharks, but on diving the deep, freshwater holes of South Australia. David was to photograph the adventure and I'd write it, but first he had to wind up his two-year shark assignment. That meant I got to go to the Coral Sea with a boatload of chum (fish guts) and film, and watch sharks get stirred into a snapping frenzy.

The Doubilets and I had met the Taylors in Rockhampton, a coastal town of Australia. Together we motored to Yeppoon where the boat *Coralita* was berthed. Ron and Valerie had been responsible for more films about sharks than just about anyone in the world. They were the principal divers and camera people in the box-office hit *Blue Water–White Death,* a cinematic search for the great white shark. They shot the underwater sequences of *Jaws* and *The Blue Lagoon* as well. Ron has the distinction of being the first man in world to film the great white shark underwater without the use of cages.

Photo by Peter Lake

*Valerie Taylor*

For the Coral Sea trip the Taylors brought along their revolutionary shark-proof suit made of a heavy metallic mesh which resembled, depending on one's sense of romance, either the chain mail of ancient knights or a fireplace curtain. It weighed about 15 pounds. Valerie was to wear it, offer herself up to the sharks and get bitten while Ron filmed it all. If everything went well, the sharks would chomp on her arms, legs and other body parts, and Valerie would come out unscathed. Valerie, a beautiful, blue-eyed blonde, wears lacy blouses with frilly collars. She hardly seems the type to get into a round of fisticuffs with sharks. Looks are deceiving. Valerie lives to tangle with the beasts. On this trip she could hardly wait to get started.

David and the Taylors were both after sharks in feeding frenzies, but their projects were separate and conflicting. Therefore, two simultaneous frenzies a day were required. Each day the two groups loaded cameras, chum and dive gear aboard their respective skiffs and headed out for their separate spots on the reef.

At Desco Reef Annie and I had gone off on our own exploring tour. That's when we were dive-bombed by territorial sharks travelling between frenzies.

I was not all that accustomed to sharks and, therefore, when I saw for myself how Valerie handled them, I was stunned. Our first day of diving had been on

*An aggressive and hungry shark
approaches the diver's cage.*

*Photo by Ron Taylor*

Swain's Reef, at the edge of the Coral Sea. When we got in the water the Taylors' assistant, Alexander, began to spear fish.

The sharks in the area, already attracted by our boat, circled around like curious dogs. As the fish were speared, they speeded up their circling. When they began to attack the speared fish, Valerie moved in to where they were feeding. She was not wearing her shark suit for these dives—the shark suit was, at this point, a secret, even from us.

Sharks are strong, muscular missiles equipped with ragged, razor-sharp teeth. They rip and tear, turn on a dime and are fiercely territorial. If they think you are a threat to them or to their chosen area, watch out! I remembered an old tip from California shark expert Don Nelson, who said that when a shark is ready to attack, its pectoral fins drop down. I found myself watching the pectoral fins of every shark I saw.

Valerie, on the other hand, loves sharks and pays no attention to pectoral fin angles. With tuna in her arms, she swam into the middle of these animals—now vibrating from side to side with the fury of the feast—and offered her hand-held bait to them. They turned from the speared fish and went for her. She proceeded to tease them, feed them, push them off with the fish and her fists. She managed to keep high the sharks' excitement for a considerable length of time.

It is astounding how quickly man becomes accustomed to situations that greatly unnerve him at the outset. Something awesome or frightful becomes acceptable, either because as a survival reflex humans instinctively calm their inner senses, or because the senses become dulled by extremes or violence. One thing is certain: excitement, no matter what its cause, even if induced by momentary fear, can be like an enslaving drug in that the excited senses want more. In other words, once you've cavorted with sharks, you're not quite as content with the slow and hapless nudibranch.

As uneasy as I felt around the sharks, I found myself wanting to see more.

Sometimes a diver won't see a shark but the shark will see the diver, and that is unpleasant to think about. Valerie explained that a shark will not usually come in for a bite (unless it's a great white). Instead, if it feels threatened, it comes in for a bump, ramming a diver with its snout to signal that the territory is not the diver's but the shark's. If the diver fails to heed the bump, then the shark may well come around for a little nip.

This particular piece of information was not very reassuring to me the afternoon Annie and I were diving on a reef seldom explored. Visibility was not good that day so we swam shallow, at about 30 feet. Around the end of the reef I heard a voice, but it was so indistinct that I thought I was hearing things. I turned around anyway, and the very act of my turning around frightened off a five-foot grey reef shark at my shoulder. It was Annie's voice I had heard. She had been yelling underwater at the top of her lungs. She later told me that the shark had made a beeline toward me as if it planned to bump me good and hard, and that I had scared it at the last minute by turning around. Because I am not Valerie Taylor by a long shot, this whole experience made my knees quake.

Four days into the expedition Valerie decided to try out the mesh suit in an area called Action Point on Marion Reef. Action Point is so named because of the way sharks behave there. Annie and I looked askance at our own suits because they looked like puny rubber outfits compared to the serious metallic mesh Valerie wore.

However, we were still intact at the end of our dive, and we were back aboard the *Coralita* waiting for the Taylors to return. When Valerie climbed aboard, we saw that her chin was black and blue. There were two holes where a shark had bitten her, leaving the tips of its teeth lodged in her jaw.

Valerie had been bitten in the head by a shark! It was mind-boggling.

"I felt a tremendous hit," said Valerie. "At the same time, the teeth hit the mesh of the suit and there was a crunching, grating sound and it was right across my ears. It sounded like it was tearing off my face." She reported this the way some people might tell their friends about going to the grocery store.

I asked Ron, who was filming the whole thing, what he had seen. "I didn't know Valerie had been hit until she went to the surface and I could see blood coming out from underneath her chin," he said. "When I'm filming, I'm not looking at the specific detail of what's happening. I'm framing, getting all the action in the frame. I never know what detail I've got until I look at the work print on the editing machine."

Ron and Valerie take such accidents in stride because it is part of the hazardous work they have chosen to do. They make a close team, for where one is, the other is close behind. Ron is the quiet one, the meditator, the thinker, the inventor. Valerie is the mover, the one who makes the business deals and keeps a shark's eye on business. The extent of her dedication to what they are trying to do could be measured by her final reaction to being bitten in the head. She smiled about it.

"It just goes to show that the shark suit really works," she said. "If the mesh had covered my chin, I reckon I wouldn't have these teeth in my jaw, now, would I?"

Later, as everyone aboard the *Coralita* slept, Valerie told me about her early experiences in the sea. What began as a hobby led her to extraordinary underwater adventures and a career that pays her well for doing what she loves best. A good career is often the marriage of avocation and occupation—hobby and job—so that work doesn't seem so much like work. A necessary ingredient to this union, however, is an unusual, individualistic approach to one's interests. In Valerie's case, it's been an unusual affinity for all sea creatures, an understanding of them on their own terms, never exploiting them or dramatizing danger by being around them. Valerie often has been a cool, abiding presence in the midst of gore, a tiny human face to face with danger.

Her career reached its present high-voltage level in 1969 with her participation in the cinematic hunt for the great white shark. She was the only woman amid a team of photographers and hordes of frenzied sharks in the box-office hit *Blue Water–White Death,* filmed during 1969 and 1970 in various oceans of the world. Armed with bangsticks, she rode shotgun over the men who were filming thousands of gnashing teeth. The expedition had been put together by American filmmaker and producer Peter Gimbel, whose goal was to search for, find and film the great white shark.

"Whitey," as the great fish is called, was most appropriately described in 1862 by Jonathan Couch, who wrote in his *Fishes of the British Islands:*

> It is to sailors the most formidable of all the inhabitants of the sea, for in none besides are the powers of inflicting injury so equally combined with the eagerness to accomplish it.[1]

Although the Gimbel expedition subjected divers to extreme hazards, they were all motivated by one thing: to capture for the first time underwater footage

Photo by Ron Taylor

*Dinghy and diver are quite close to a traveling shark (above), and the shark (below) becomes quite interested in Valerie Taylor and the prospect of another meal.*

Photo by Ron Taylor

*Photo by Ron Taylor*

*Valerie Taylor's mesh suit is her protection from a biting shark.*

of Whitey. Valerie had gone along simply to accompany Ron, but she ended up being the most unusual star of the film—unusual because one does not usually see an angel in such harrowing situations.

Born in Sydney, Australia in 1936, Valerie has been diving for over 30 years. Because her parents had a waterfront home, she found it easy to begin snorkeling. She began spearfishing and by 1963 had won the Australian Women's Spearfishing Open Championship three times. The last competition she entered was in 1968.

"I realized that spearfishing was a bad thing," she said. "It really is. They get boatloads of all kinds of fish and most are wasted. Ron and I noticed how the fish life became depleted as more and more people began spearfishing, and we stopped."

Ron Taylor is a veteran underwater filmmaker and, when the Taylors quit spearfishing, they both turned to making a living in underwater photography. For Ron's photographs and films, Valerie often played with sea animals in an attempt to bring them closer to Ron's lens, and also to understand the animals better.

The Taylors found their new career rough going at first, because at the time no one in Australia seemed interested in sea films. Their first break came when

84

*Photo by Peter Lake*

*The sharks here clearly outnumber Valerie Taylor.*

the Belgium University at Liege hired them for a six-month scientific expedition to the Great Barrier Reef. Then when Peter Gimbel put together his expedition to film the great white, the Taylors were natural choices. Ron had already filmed white sharks—without cages—and he had captured some of the most dramatic and exciting footage of these animals ever recorded. He agreed to join the expedition on the condition that Valerie could accompany him. The group consisted of Gimbel, filmmaker Stan Waterman, Peter Matthiessen (author of the book, *Blue Meridian,* about the expedition), still photographer Peter Lake, topside cameraman Jim Lipscomb, sound man Stuart Cody, production manager Phil Clarkson, key grip Tom Chapin, and the Taylors. They met aboard the whale catcher *Terrier* and set out for the Indian Ocean.

Valerie kept a daily journal, which Matthiessen referred to as he wrote his book. In her journal, Valerie describes how she hung suspended in a black sea on a black night in a cage surrounded by sharks. The sharks had come in to feed on a whale carcass that was slung alongside the *Terrier.* Gimbel was filming the action from the cage he shared with Valerie, while Ron and Stan Waterman worked from another cage. The sea was rough. A huge, fifteen-foot tiger shark appeared. Its head was almost three feet wide. It made a beeline toward one of the 5,000-watt lights hanging 45 feet below Valerie's cage. It swallowed the entire lamp and spat it out.

The rough seas created a more serious problem: the electrical lines of the cages began to cross and tangle. When the two cages banged together, their tethers became tangled, putting the divers in a precarious spot. She wrote:

> Our cage-tethering rope was longer than the power cable, and it took all my time and strength to keep hold of the thing. We were tied to the *Terrier,* which didn't help matters much. Her rise and fall was ten times that of the whale. Peter, realizing my difficulty, helped me pull a length of cable into the cage and hook it around a valve on the far cylinder. This put a big strain on the valve, but we managed to shoot and light a few scenes before the strain became so great as to endanger the cage.[2]

Finally Valerie and Peter lost their lights altogether as they pulled completely away from the cage. Ron and Stan had problems of their own. Their light cable had entangled around the whale. From there it had wrapped around the buoyancy tanks of Valerie's and Peter's cage. They lost their lights, too. On the surface, Stuart Cody saw the problem and cut the cages free of the ship before proceeding to untangle the twisted mess of cables. Sharks continued to swarm outside.

> In the cage, we didn't realize our predicament. We just sat there waiting. I wondered why we weren't able to see the whale anymore and why our light had faded and why I couldn't hear the heart of the ship beating away. I didn't realize that we were no longer tethered to anything but just drifting freely at night, surrounded by feeding sharks.[3]

Cody got the tangle straightened and secured the cages to the *Terrier.* The lights came back on. Almost immediately a nine-foot whitetip shark became ensnared in the cables on top of Valerie's cage. As it thrashed around, she and Peter were buffeted from side to side like a pair of dice. The shark twisted its way free. But before any of them could think of what to do next, both cages drifted into the whale.

> Ribbons of mutilated intestines streamed through the bars as the cages clanged together where the sharks had opened the whale's body. Ron was wrestling to keep his cage free from the jaw bone. I couldn't see him for the blood and gore. It turned the scene into sort of raw soup. Although it was impossible, I thought I was breathing and tasting the stuff. I don't know how we ever got free of the whale, but I know that it was so pleasant to be away from that torn, smelling hulk that I felt happy.[4]

86

*A visit with an octopus and sea lions can be friendlier than a visit with sharks.*

By this time Peter and Stan, in their different cages, were running out of air. The Zodiac picked up Stan and Ron from their cage and, as they left the water, the sharks attacked the cables with renewed frenzy.

"Then suddenly, without warning," Valerie wrote, "a tremendous shock vibrated through our cage. Peter and I had drifted into the ship's hull." As both cages crashed against the *Terrier* in the rough seas, Valerie and Peter were freed from its confines. "I couldn't vacate the darn thing fast enough," Valerie said.[5]

This brush with disaster would seem more than enough, but the drama was outdone by an even more dire situation that left those who took part in it in a state of disbelief even to this day. On May 4, 1969, in a spot off Durban, South Africa, while looking for Whitey, the group chummed the open ocean with dead whale from the *Terrier* and waited for action. Soon the waters were churning with about 200 sharks. The men prepared the cages and were ready to enter the water when Peter Gimbel announced that he was going to get out of his cage once they submerged. Valerie knew she would follow his lead, but not without trepidation.

> I looked at all those sharks swimming around; it was a very nice day, the sun was shining, and I thought: Well, today we are all going to get killed. I stood there on the deck and looked about at the crew and thought about

87

everything—about my nephews and nieces back in Australia that I loved so much and the rest of the family. I thought: Have a good look at everything, because I don't think I'll get out of the cage and survive.[6]

Then, in their cages, they entered the water. Valerie watched sharks tear big chunks out of the whale. Blood poured from their gills as they gulped and thrashed around with whale guts hanging from their mouths. Valerie felt no fear, she said, only excitement.

Then Peter swam out of the cage he shared with Valerie. She didn't close the door at first, but sat on the floor of the cage thinking she would actually see him killed right then and there. But she felt she would have to help him. The sharks began to bump him around and Peter beat them off with his camera. Stan Waterman left his cage. Peter, always the gentleman, returned and led Valerie out into the open. Soon they were all beating off the sharks, making themselves accepted as other marine creatures that had come to feed on the whale.

Valerie's ability to make herself as one with marine creatures has led her into a number of dramatic situations. It also made her a dynamic subject of the underwater camera. She hates killing anything in the sea, even sharks. She is happiest when she can pet moray eels on the head, play with an octopus or feed barracuda by hand. She has an uncanny way of befriending sea creatures, and she uses it when she's in front of the camera, as well as when she is behind it.

"I always seem to end up with a couple of marine creatures who are my friends," she said. "This is one of my greatest pleasures, having a fish swim up and look at me with curiosity and we have a little conversation. Every living thing has feelings. So I give all the corals, shells and fish their due; they're busy getting along, busy in their little ways. I figure if I'm nice to them, they will be nice to me."[7]

Valerie once had two moray eels for friends, nicknamed Harry and Fang. They knew her and she always carried something for them to eat when she went to see them. She often picked up Harry, who was as big as she is, and took him to the surface to show him to people sitting in the boat. Harry bit two photographers, however, and Valerie thought it was because they handled him too roughly.

Valerie has been featured on the covers of national magazines, once with an octopus sitting on her head, and again holding a poisonous sea snake. While she appears to be totally fearless, she admits that she is often afraid. Curiosity is what motivates her, and her curiosity reached its peak when the *Blue Water–White*

*Photo by Ron Taylor*

*A three and one-half hour frolic with the giant whale shark (above) requires far less protection than does a visit with the great white (below).*

*Photo by Ron Taylor*

*Death* expedition finally met the great white shark. As the killer swam by her cage, Valerie reached out and stroked its belly.

Valerie is a competent photographer. In the past, Time-Life has used her to shoot still photos around the Virgin Islands for its wilderness series. She has written books, most notably *Underwater World.* She has starred in both U.S. and foreign television series. Both above and below the water she and Ron filmed all of the live shark segments for *Jaws* (I and II). Among their notable Hollywood credits are the films *Orca* and *Blue Lagoon.* Today, they continue to film for various countries all over the world.

When asked if she has trouble making a living in what is considered a male-dominated field, Valerie says that she doesn't. "I seem to have some sort of sixth sense about fish and other animals. I seem to know if I can approach a shark or if I should be out of the water. Some people think I'm not afraid. Sometimes I'm awfully afraid, but I have a tremendous curiosity."[8]

In the summer of 1981, Ron and Valerie were diving off the coast of California, near San Clemente Island, as part of a short segment for the ABC television series, *Those Amazing Animals.* The waters were chummed for blue sharks. Eventually they came in and Valerie went diving with them. As she was watching a shark swim above her head, another blue shark came up from below and bit her leg. Back on deck, Valerie viewed her wound with a philosophical calm. "I asked for it," she said. "I've been very lucky all this time."

Valerie disapproves of shark-mania and doesn't view them as killers. "The great white is nature's garbageman," she says, "efficient, inexpensive and nonpolluting. His job is to keep the ocean free from large masses of garbage. Be it dead whale or cardboard box, the great white devours all, leaving the ocean cleaner with his passing."[9]

The Taylors have also turned their attention to the matter of marine conservation. In 1971 they began to work through Australian government channels to create a marine preserve on the Great Barrier Reef, in an area off Lizard Island. The area, which the Taylors named the Cod Hole, was full of big, friendly fish called potato cods, a type of grouper. When Ron and Valerie saw the fish they had befriended being speared, they began to petition the government. Today the Cod Hole is a marine park, and Valerie was given a government award for her efforts in establishing it. Her real reward, she said, is in the fact that her fish friends can live out their lives in peace.

In May, 1987 Valerie sent me a letter containing some advice she wanted to pass on to those just starting out in the field. She says:

> It's a hard road to start from nothing as we did. I think the most important thing is to not expect too much in the beginning. We get letters, hundreds of them, all the time from all over the world from young people wanting to do what we do. They want to come and work with us, shooting film, diving, travelling. No one has ever written offering to fill tanks, carry cameras, mash bait, sort slides, clean the boat, wash the dishes. They don't seem to realize how much time (15 years actually) we spent selling fish around camping areas, spearing fish for commercial companies and putting on our own underwater shows just to get the money to buy film. It doesn't happen like magic. You must always deliver the goods, even if it costs you, and you can't expect too much. Be grateful for what little you get. Do everything with a smile.[10]

## Notes

1. Jonathan Couch, *Fishes of the British Islands,* 1862 (out of print).
2. From the personal journal of Valerie Taylor, 1969.
3. Peter Matthiessen, *Blue Meridian* (Random House: New York, 1971), pp. 73-74.
4. *Op. cit.,* Valerie Taylor's journal.
5. *Ibid.*
6. *Ibid.*
7. Personal communication to Hillary Hauser from Valerie Taylor.
8. *Ibid.*
9. Interview of Valerie Taylor by Hillary Hauser, August 1981.
10. Letter from Valerie Taylor to Hillary Hauser, May 25, 1987.

## Suggested Reading

Valerie Taylor, ``A Jawbreaker for Sharks'' (*National Geographic Magazine,* May 1981).
Ron & Valerie Taylor, *Underwater World* (Ure Smith: Sydney, 1976).
Peter Matthiessen, *Blue Meridian* (Random House: New York, 1971).
Richard Ellis, *The Book of Sharks* (Grosset & Dunlap: New York, 1976).

## Chapter 9

# The Sinkholes of Australia

*The vitality of thought
is in adventure. Ideas won't keep.
Something must be done
about them.*

— *Alfred North Whitehead*

After the *Coralita* docked in Yeppoon, David, Annie and I flew back to Melbourne from Rockhampton, exchanged our warm-water wetsuits for very cold-water wetsuits, and flew to Mt. Gambier in South Australia.

Mt. Gambier is a small town built around a volcano, located about halfway between Adelaide and Melbourne. It is a friendly place where locals trip over each other to get an earful of Yankee accents and where sheep ranchers in terry cloth hats meet at the end of each day in country pubs to swap stories. The countryside of Mt. Gambier itself is a composite of sheep stations, pine forests, lakes and the sinkholes we were going to explore.

Our guide to the deep, flooded caves of Mt. Gambier was Rodney Fox, a well-known Australian diver who had miraculously survived the savage attack of a great white shark. After his attack Rodney had tested his lungs—which had been severely lacerated by the shark—by free diving in the deep underwater chasm of Piccaninnie Ponds, one of the principal spots of our story.

When we arrived at "Pics", as the locals call the hole, we were met by a croaking chorus of half submerged frogs in a marsh swamp surrounding the jetty. The South Australian sky was ominously grey and bitter cold air blew from the Southern Ocean two miles away. I pulled my collar up around my face and walked

93

out onto the jetty of the pond, past the frogs which quickly withdrew into their shallow puddle of slime and broken reeds.

We unloaded the camera equipment and diving gear from Rodney's Land Rover, then changed into our diving suits standing on a tarp. Without the tarp we would have been ankle deep in mud.

Soon we were swimming away from the Piccaninnie jetty across the first pond. I dropped down to ten feet into a mystical world of green algae. A school of tiny trout-like fish swam by and proceeded to pick on a floating clump of moss. The water was cold and so crystal clear that I could see to the far edge of the pond.

The three of us followed David toward a neat row of reedy plants that were so perfectly aligned they seemed planted on purpose as a sort of underwater stage curtain. We swam through the reeds.

On the other side, we were instantly suspended over an enormous flooded crack in the earth—100 feet deep, 150 feet long and 20 feet wide. The water was so transparent I felt suspended in air, as if I were soaring through a Grand Canyon of deep blue. The drop-off was so unexpected and surprising that I yelled into my regulator, but no one heard. We were in the Piccaninnie Chasm.

I swam past the filamentous yellow-green algae which hung down on either side of the precipitous walls of the chasm. In the deep, blue abyss below me I saw the limestone teeth that jutted out from the walls. I free-fell past the teeth to 90 feet. To the right of me a cave slanted off at 45 degrees. In the cave I turned on my light and saw a series of narrowing slots that dropped to 187 feet. This was what the locals called the Dog Leg. I sank into the dark crack and stopped at 125 feet. My light created eerie shadows and pockets in the blackness below. There was no bottom to be seen. I'd heard of the diver who died in this hole at 177 feet, tangled hopelessly in the monofilament line he'd been using as a safety line. I turned back and swam toward the light.

I caught up with the others at the far end of the chasm and we swam inside the Cathedral, a huge, moonlike cave. A tiny fish swam in front of my light, casting a giant shadow on a limestone wall. I looked at Annie. She was photographing something on top of a limestone pinnacle near the entrance of the cave. It was the partially exposed shell of an ancient, fossilized sea urchin embedded in the limestone.

Russell Kitt arrived in Mt. Gambier the next afternoon, excited and ready to lead us into some of the more restricted holes of Mt. Gambier. Russell is president of the Cave Divers Association of Australia, and no one without a permit from the CDAA goes into the holes of Mt. Gambier. If a diver is caught in Piccaninnie without a permit, the park ranger confiscates his equipment. Most of the other holes around Mt. Gambier are on private property, but landowners don't allow divers into their holes without permits either.

Photo by Hillary Hauser

Photo by Hillary Hauser

*The approach to Piccaninnie Ponds*

*A topside view of the ladder leading down into the Shaft.*

Why the restrictions? Because divers have died. Two in Kilsby's, two in Piccaninnie, three in Death Cave, and finally, four in the Shaft. The Shaft incident in 1973, which took all four lives at one time, was the last straw. The Australian government threatened to shut down all the holes of Mt. Gambier completely when the CDAA organized in 1974. The group proposed a special training/permit system for cave diving which they insisted would be effective. The government agreed to give it a try. So far, the system has worked. Russell Kitt insists on strict adherence to the rules. No one can bypass the tests necessary to get permits. No one. We'd gone through a special process to get permits in Melbourne.

Russell wanted to show us some of the holes designated "Category Three." Category One describes the safe holes open to the sky. Category Two holes contain some submerged passageways (Piccaninnie is a "Cat Two"). The Category Three holes have more complicated submerged passageways and silting conditions. It's not hard to get lost in a passageway underwater when one cannot see. For Category Three holes, you have to have lights and safety lines. And you have to know what you are doing.

Bullock Hole, so named for a cow that fell into it at one time, was a fairly big pit in the middle of the Barnoolut sheep station and is designated as a Category

Photo by David Doubilet

*Reaching a sinkhole could mean a 30 foot climb down a rope ladder (right). Divers explore an area called "The Cathedral" and Piccaninnie Ponds. Nine strobe lights were required to pervade the darkness (opposite page).*

Three hole. Russell and I drove out together in his lime-green station wagon, with Rodney Fox and the Doubilets following close behind. As we bounced over the sheep pasture, Russell talked animatedly about what we were going to see. He was excited about everything. He is a high-strung, Australian version of Giancarlo Giannini—dark, bearded, his mind working all the time.

It was a 30-foot drop to the water. Russell rigged up a mountaineering ladder attached to the fender of Rodney's Land Rover, draped over the ledge of the hole and down toward the water. Inside the hole birds flew in and out of their nests, crisscrossing each other just above the water's surface. A dead bird floated in a film of pasture grass blown in by the winds. Broken eggshells were strewn about at the base of the walls.

David, Russell and I geared up in our heavy wetsuits, in the heat, in the middle of a sheep pasture, to dive in with the dead bird and floating pasture grass.

When I started down the ladder, I realized it was not going to be such an easy situation. I realized, too, that it was going to be even worse climbing out. The ladder started to swivel and turn, and my legs became weak and wobbly. In my heavy wetsuit I could feel the perspiration pouring down my back, my legs and my chest. It was almost 100° outside, the hottest day of the year.

*Photo by David Doubilet*

Our equipment and David's cameras were lowered down. After we strapped ourselves into our tanks and regulators, we dropped beneath the surface. We were in an enormous chamber of transparent water, so clear that I could see the bottom below me at 100 feet. We sank down to 50 feet. I looked up and through the water saw the outline of the top of the hole with Annie standing at the edge of it. It was like being in an encapsulized, magical world of Beowulf—a chamber beneath a lake where heroes and dragons live out imaginary lives.

Unlike Piccaninnie Ponds, there is no life in Bullock's, but that was not the point. The entire adventure was to drop down into an underground, underwater chamber and explore. We were diving in a cavern that had been formed by the Miocene ocean that once had owned the land, an ocean that now lapped at the shores of Port MacDonnell over ten miles away.

The origin of holes like Bullock and Piccaninnie is an interesting geological phenomenon. In the Miocene epoch, 10 to 30 million years ago, the whole of South Australia was underwater. During those millions of years, sea animals lived and died. Their skeletons carpeted the ocean floor layer upon layer until the calcified carbonate material was transformed into an enormous mass of limestone. Then the oceans receded, the limestone layer became dry land, and the rains came down. In Australia, the rainfall from the Victoria and Penola Plains

97

to the north permeated the limestone, running toward the ocean in the direction of Mt. Gambier. Contained in rainwater is carbon dioxide, which dissolves limestone. As the water collected in ever-enlarging pools underground, the limestone bedrock dissolved. In some areas the surface land collapsed to form sinkholes, such as Piccaninnie and Bullock Hole.

We dived for over an hour in Bullock Hole, David taking pictures of Russell and me exploring the main cavern. The water was frigid, and I was glad for my heavy wetsuit, even if I'd nearly passed out from the heat on the way down.

When the three of us surfaced, the fun really began. We had to climb out—up that 30-foot ladder and over a ledge at the top. Even though our tanks, fins and weightbelts were hauled up separately, getting up that wild, bucking ladder was a monstrous feat. Each rung required a pull of one's total body weight by a single arm or leg. For the last five steps I could barely close my hands. They were freezing from the ice-cold water and paralyzed from hanging on so hard. My forearm muscles went into spasms. I was almost to the top of the ladder when I realized I might not make it, no matter how hard I tried. I yelled for help, but there wasn't anything anyone could do. Rodney stood at the rim of the ledge, taking pictures and laughing at my plight. I absolutely knew that I didn't want to fall 30 feet back into the hole. Finally Rodney realized I wasn't kidding and came over to the top of the ladder to encourage me on and up. I drew myself up until he could grasp my arms, enough to pull me over the top. The second I was on solid ground, I instantly collapsed into a heap in the grass.

Russell scaled the ladder unaided, as if he did it every day of the year. No telling what he thought of these flimsy Americans.

As Russell and I drove away from Bullock Hole, he made some suggestions as to what we should dive next. First, he said, we should dive One Tree. "I reckon that will really give you the feeling of what cave diving is all about," he said. "In fact, let's do it right now."

I agreed to the plan right away. We waved the others goodbye and a few minutes later, down the road, Russell pulled into the Bellum Bellum, a country pub near Mt. Schank where ranchers unwind after a hard day's work. He figured we'd find Peter Norman there, and it was from Peter Norman we needed permission to dive One Tree.

Russell figured right. Peter was there, wearing his characteristic terry cloth hat. "No worries!" he said. "She's all yours!" He not only gave us his permission to dive, but he invited us for a dinner of mutton the next night.

One Tree is marked by one big, lonely tree in the middle of an open field. The sun was setting as Russell and I climbed down to the water, about 15 feet below tree level. Russell put a line with a clip around my left wrist, then we sank beneath

*Hillary Hauser inspects the bubbling sands on the bottom of Ewens Pond.*

the surface. I attached the wrist clip to the orange safety line Russell reeled out as he swam in front of me.

It grew darker and darker as we went down. Our flashlight beams searched the green-black water. When we reached 90 feet, Russell wrapped the safety line around the limb of a tree which lay on its side on the bottom. We looked up. All there was to see was a lighter murky green toward the surface and our safety line trailing up and out of sight. Then we turned toward the darkness again and swam along a ledge into a cave which went in for about 90 feet and down to a depth of 135 feet. It was black. And cold. We explored the cave, our light picking up the bottom and sides of the hole. Then we saw an overturned car. It lay on the bottom—eerie, dark, mysterious.

Russell now indicated that we were ready to turn around, so I unclipped myself from the safety line and swam behind him to follow him out. The only thing wrong with this plan was that Russell had the reel and there would be no line behind him on the way out. It took me a while to realize this. I was completely "narked" and didn't know it.

"Mate, if that wasn't nitrogen narcosis, what is?" Russell said later. He was amused by what had happened, but then became serious. "You should never, never unclip yourself from the safety line," he said. "*Never!*" Nitrogen narcosis, or "the raptures of the deep", is a serious problem in cave diving. It can cause misjudgment, and it is misjudgment that causes trouble—like getting lost or running out of air. It had killed the four divers in the Shaft.

When I first saw the Shaft several days later, I laughed in disbelief. It is a hole with a tiny opening the size of a city manhole, in the middle of a pasture so large there is nothing to see for miles but grass. Two other members of the Cave Divers Association had arrived to dive with us, since the Shaft had not been opened to divers since 1973 when the four deaths occurred. Mr. and Mrs. B. V. Ashby, who own the land there, were troubled deeply about that accident, which had claimed the lives of a brother and sister at one time. They still hadn't gotten over it. Even so, they were allowing us to dive.

I looked down the manhole-sized opening and it looked terribly dark and dismal inside. David looked up at the sky and surveyed the situation. Patches of clouds were flying by and building on the horizon.

"Let's hope for some sun," he said.

Russell was first into the hole and I followed him. It wasn't until I got down that mountaineering ladder 25 feet to the water that I got my first real look at where we were. We were inside a large, air-filled chamber lit by the daylight shining down that narrow opening and reflecting from the water to the ceiling. It wasn't dark and gloomy at all. Although clouds were blocking the sun, it remained light inside, the small opening to the surface a natural lamp in the enormous domed ceiling.

Suddenly the sun broke through the clouds, and Russell and I witnessed the phenomenon for which the hole is famous. A powerful shaft of light, thrown through the small opening at the top of the chamber, beamed through the clear, black water in a bright, iridescent blue. It shone all the way down to the first ledge below us at 120 feet. It was brilliant from above the water, but underwater it was almost blinding. With the dark water around it clear and in a chamber as big as a small coliseum, it was difficult to tell the depth we were in. I thought I was at 30 feet when I was at 60. At 70 feet I thought the bottom was just beyond my fins when it was actually another 50 feet down. I was beginning to understand about the four divers who disappeared in this hole.

Russell Kitt returned to Melbourne, and his assistant, John McCormick, led us on our next dive. The Pines is a Category Three hole set in the middle of a forest. The top of the water looked green and swampy, and while the four of us slogged around knee deep in mud, I was convinced that it would never be deep enough anywhere to dive. An overhang of forest floor loomed in front of us. Just at the foot of it, John sank down and disappeared. I followed, and underneath that ledge was a large opening which took us into a huge underwater cavern. The floor of this chamber sloped downward to about 60 feet. John, Annie and I explored the flooded room with our lights while David took photographs. The grafitti on the walls struck us as very odd, since we were deep underground, far from the reaches of average humanity.

John and I left the others and continued down into a crack at the far side of the cavern floor. The crack opened up into a narrow passageway that weaved

100

down, up and around to its end. John reeled out the safety line and I stayed close, the clip on my wrist sliding down the line behind him. We were in a narrow, flooded corridor. I wanted to see what was in front of John, so I beamed my strong underwater light over his shoulder as we swam.

I was exhilarated beyond anything I'd ever known. In cave diving there is a feeling of wonder, the excitement of finding a hidden nook somewhere, the tight squeezes, the feeling of hanging suspended in air, and more than anything else— discovery. It is the crystallization of every feeling one gets from adventure, the heart of what it is that propels one to explore something new.

John and I continued to dive as many holes as we could around Mt. Gambier. Together we dived the Ela Elap hole on Peter Norman's property and went into Allendale, a flooded cave in the middle of a road between two lanes of traffic. For the Allendale hole we had to gear up by the side of the road and run across the highway as cars passed by on either side. Since the hole was not visible from the road, some people slowed and stared unabashedly. To them we were only a couple of water-hungry people running around in the middle of a dry countryside in hopes, perhaps, of heavy rain.

The *coup de grace* came when I fell down the dirt embankment toward the hole as we were climbing out after the dive. Somehow I missed a step, and by missing a step with a scuba tank on my back, I was as helpless as an overturned turtle. I rolled downhill like a log cut loose, and by the time I got back up to the top of the embankment again, I was a towering statue of mud. To my great fortune, there was a faucet just outside the fence surrounding the hole, and John proceeded to provide me with a shower by filling up his fins and throwing water at me. A car went by, saw us and stopped down the road in Allendale to report at the general store that they had seen a couple of hard-up divers playing in the faucet. Vilma, the general store owner, laughed about it to us later. She said the people were really mystified. Their confusion was to be expected. How were they to know that underneath the highway was one of the underwater wonders of Australia?

The travellers, said Vilma, finally settled on the idea that we had been in the countryside too long and were lonesome for the ocean.

### Suggested Reading

Hillary Hauser, "Exploring a Sunken Realm in Australia" (*National Geographic Magazine*, January 1984).

*Chapter 10*

*Rodney Fox*

# Rodney Fox:
# From the Jaws of Death

*Mishaps are like knives, that*
*either serve us or cut us,*
*as we grasp them*
*by the blade or the handle.*

— *James Russell Lowell*

D ecember 8, 1963. Aldinga Beach, South Australia. Rodney Fox was in the water, concentrating on a fish that hid in the seagrass below. He was floating midwater, holding his breath, watching his target, moving closer and closer to the fish, his speargun aimed.

Suddenly he was hit as if by a train. He felt the clasp of jaws that held him with razor-sharp teeth. The teeth belonged to a great white shark.

One of the best things to come out of the *National Geographic* assignment in Australia was the opportunity to get to know Rodney Fox, who had been our guide and location manager for the story on Piccaninnie Ponds. I'd heard of Rodney for years because of his shark attack, and because, in spite of that terrible experience, he had gone on to make great white sharks his specialty. Rodney Fox is an example of how a person can benefit from misfortune, if he or she is determined to learn from it rather than to fear its recurrence.

Rodney nearly died from his shark attack, yet he has led teams of photographers and Hollywood film crews to document great white sharks. He organized the filming of them for *Jaws* and other cinematic dramas. In Australia, he is a celebrity. After his attack, children looked up to him, adults knew him on the streets, in the news, on television.

General curiosity surrounds a man who has been attacked by a shark. People want to look at the scar; they want to ask about it. Usually they don't, because most people feel timid about asking such things.

The first time we changed into our diving suits at Piccaninnie Ponds, I noticed Rodney's scar. It was hard not to notice, since it envelops the left side of his body,

103

stretching from above his underarm to below his rib cage in a big "U"—a scar shaped like the jaws of a shark.

One rainy afternoon in Mt. Gambier, when we couldn't dive Piccaninnie Ponds or anywhere else, Rodney and I sat together, and I asked him to tell me the story of his shark attack. Big, friendly and mischievous, Rodney took a big breath and smiled as if he had a prank up his sleeve. "Which version do you want?" he asked. "The half-hour one, or the one-and-a-half-hour one?" I told him to spare no detail.

"I knew it was a shark," he began. "It had its jaws clamped around my back and chest, and I was being hurled through the water." He described reaching around, trying to gouge the eyes of the shark, when suddenly—inexplicably— it let him go. He pushed off from the animal with his right arm, but the arm disappeared down the shark's mouth. The teeth tore it to shreds, severing four tendons and rendering his right hand completely useless.

He struggled to the surface where he took a big gasp of air and looked down. What he saw was a sea of his own blood, and then, to his horror, he saw the shark coming up toward him from below, its mouth open, its big, conical teeth bared.

"I thought I was gone," he said.

He kicked out with his flippers as hard as he could, believing that he might have to sacrifice a foot or leg. "It knocked the shiver out of me," Rodney said.

The shark veered off and in doing so, swallowed the surface float line attached to Rodney's weightbelt. When the shark came to the end of the line, it began to drag Rodney through the water at breakneck speed. He was swirled around and around at the end of the line, all the while losing blood and struggling for air. With his left hand, he began to reach around for the quick-release buckle of his weightbelt, but the buckle had been pulled to the back and he couldn't reach it. At the point he was ready to breathe water, the line snapped. The shark had bitten it just enough to cause a break at the critical moment.

This stroke of luck gave Rodney an extra boost of encouragement to hold on for air. He wasn't sure which way was up, but he told himself to relax and drift up as naturally as a leaf drifts down from a tree.

In a matter of moments, he broke the surface, and now he screamed. His cry for help was heard by divers in a nearby boat. Almost immediately they had him aboard, heading for shore.

"Now I realized how serious it all was because of the concern I heard in people's voices," Rodney said. "I was having trouble breathing and I was really quite a mess."

What he didn't know what that all the ribs on his left side were crushed, the left lung collapsed, his shoulder blade pierced by a tooth.

The shoreline at Aldinga Beach, where Rodney was diving, is backed by a very high cliff. Beyond the sand lies a horseshoe-shaped reef which is exposed much

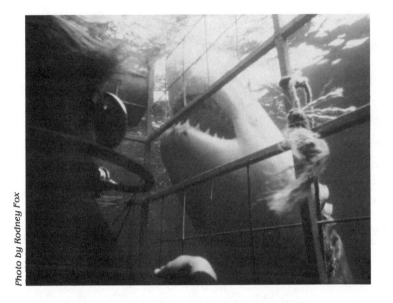

*Photo by Rodney Fox*

*The great white attacks the cage
in feeding frenzy.*

of the time, meaning that divers must walk carefully over the sharp rocks that can slice bare feet to shreds. On that particular day, someone had brought his car onto the beach because he was "sick and tired" of hauling his equipment up and down the cliff. It was the first time the sand and rocks had been suitable to bring a car into the area for many years. Meanwhile, a friend, Bruce Farley, took off barefoot over the reef for help. The first person he encountered was an off-duty policeman who knew exactly what to do. Later Farley realized that he had run across a reef of rocks, barnacles and shells without so much as a scratch to his feet.

Rodney recalled being lifted into the car, whereupon his whole left side opened up. His friends quickly turned him the other way and his friend, Malcolm Baker, pushed him back together. They got him into the car and sped down the beach and up toward the road.

"That's when the pain started to settle in," said Rodney. "I now knew I couldn't do much for myself, so I let myself go into their hands. That's when the pain began."

In the car he was having difficulty breathing, every breath giving him no air at all. Malcolm Baker sat beside him, shouting, "Keep trying, Rodney, keep fighting! Remember Kay and the baby. Come on, you've got to keep breathing!"

They encountered the ambulance going the other way. "I was really only half there and I was sucking in air and making funny noises," Rodney recalled. "I thought I would pass out, but tried hard not to. Once I was put into the ambulance, I thought it would be easier, but it wasn't. They gave me oxygen, but

Photo by Rodney Fox

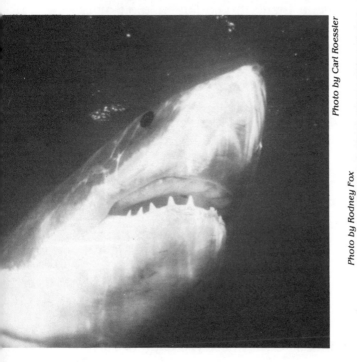

Photo by Carl Roessler

Photo by Rodney Fox

The giant predator stalks the cage (top), leers hungrily (left,) and attacks (above).

# RODNEY FOX: FROM THE JAWS OF DEATH

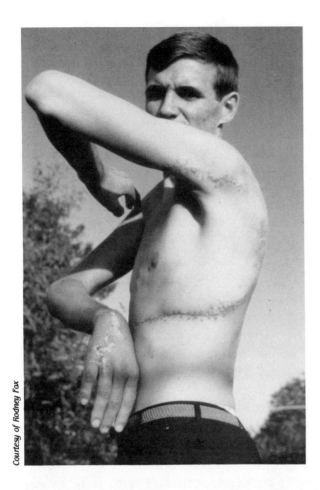

Courtesy of Rodney Fox

*Rodney Fox survived the shark attack but carries many scars as a reminder (above). The great white (below) continues to move through the water, insatiable and unforgiving.*

Photo by Carl Roessler

I still had to breathe it, and just breathing was the hardest thing I can ever remember."

Every stoplight was manned by the police. The ambulance never slowed down during the 38 miles from Aldinga to Adelaide. From the time he had been attacked to the time he reached the hospital was less than an hour. Five minutes more, said the doctors, and all his veins would have collapsed.

In the hospital, they quickly cut off his wetsuit and prepared him for emergency surgery. Someone called for a priest. "That did it!" said Rodney. He was half conscious, drugged and mutilated, but he pushed himself up on the operating table. "I'm *Protestant!*" he complained.

Rodney laughed as he remembered it. "Well," he said, "I reckon they had to know there was life in the old boy, yet!"

The next thing he remembers is regaining consciousness on the operating table. Oxygen was being pumped into his right lung. While he lay there, he became aware of a light over his head, "a long, rectangular boxlike light," Rodney recalled. "I could see this light with my eyes open or closed. I thought I was feeling okay, everything was sort of stable. Then all of a sudden my chest started to go down and down and down. There was all sorts of commotion and swearing about the oxygen supply being switched over. The box started to get smaller and smaller and smaller."

At this moment he began to experience flashbacks. "The flashbacks were things I had done wrong. I recalled stealing marbles as a boy, lighting a fire that nobody ever found out about that burned five or six acres. Things like that."

Was this his day of reckoning? Rodney thought it might have been.

"It's nothing supernatural," he said. "I believe that those things were wrong, but if they're the only things that come back to my mind at that point, I reckon I haven't got much to worry about."

Then the rectangular box of light started to return, larger and larger. His chest rose up again with the renewed oxygen supply, the light box stabilized, and the flashbacks ceased.

His next recollection was the recovery room. "I was in there for seven or eight days," he said. "I was a little frightened because other people were being shifted in and out, but I stayed and stayed. I had a silent fear there was something they weren't telling me."

What they weren't telling him was that they were waiting for him to go into shock. The doctors expected that to be his biggest problem. They also worried that the shark's teeth might have contained some strange microbe that could create problems in his body. They kept him shot up with antibiotics to ward off infection and drugged him to ward off pain. His job was to breathe.

*Dr. Sylvia Earle and Deep Rover*

*Valerie Taylor's underwater excursions allow her to greet Harry (left), a faithful friend since 1970, and work with sea lions (below). She appreciates the advantage of wearing a mesh suit, when in the company of sharks. (right).*

The sinkholes of Australia can offer excellent diving conditions. As divers swim across the chasm of Piccaninnie Ponds (left), the crystal clear water allows the clouds in the sky to remain visible. A diver swims along the sandy algae-covered bottom of Ewens Ponds (right). Divers prepare to enter The Pines (below).

*Looking straight down from the top of the Titanic (right), a photo taken from the towed camera sled Angus reveals a tear and collapsed decks on the forward section's starboard side. The hull is buckled outward, showing windows into the liner's promenades. Below "rusticicles" — icicles of rust — nearly cover a porthole. Two bollards (bottom) were used to secure mooring lines.*

*Jason Jr. leaves Alvin (left) and photographs the remains of the luxury liner Titanic (below).*

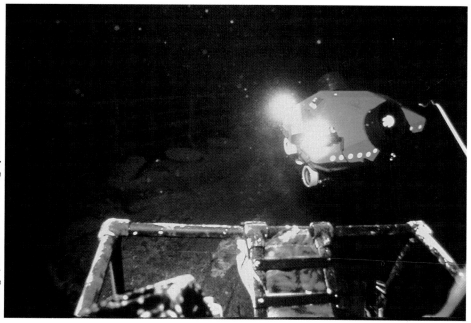

Courtesy of Cousteau Society

*Jacques Cousteau*

Photo by Carl Roessler

*The great white shark: a powerful and voracious predator.*

Shock never did set in. A large part of this was due to his excellent physical condition, and this is one of the biggest reasons he is alive today. Another equally important reason for his survival, the doctors said, was his mental condition.

"I think there are two kinds of shock," Rodney reasoned. "One from the actual attack to the body, and the other from a fear and shock to the mind. A friend of mine had been attacked by a shark, and we had discussed it many times. We knew of the problems if there was an attack, and I think I was able to accept what was happening. I figured I just had to wait it out."

All in all, the doctors put 462 stitches in his left side, 92 stitches in his right hand, and repaired severed tendons, broken bones, torn muscles and collapsed arteries. Miraculously, the teeth of the shark had just missed his heart, main artery and his spleen.

"A fraction of an inch to the left and that would have been it," Rodney said, slashing his throat with his finger.

His healing was quick. After two weeks he was unwrapped, and there was a fine layer of skin over everything, no infections. The doctors were amazed. He went home and continued to heal, working with physical therapists to bring his body and lung capacity back to normal. He wasn't sure about when he would go back into the water. When newspaper reporters continued to ask him about it, he shrugged it off and told them he didn't know.

"Three months after I was attacked," said Rodney, "on a beautiful, sunny day, Kay and I went to a skin-diving club meeting. We had a great big surfboard that we could sit on and we went out. I slipped on my mask and flippers and stuck my head over the side. About 15 to 18 feet down was a nice fish so I took one breath and headed down. My chest hurt, but I speared and brought up the fish."

Did he think about sharks?

"I swivel-necked around," he answered. "It was difficult."

His first encounter with a shark after his attack was a pivotal moment. Six months after his reentry into the sea, he went with friends Bruce Farley and Brian Rodgers on a lobster boat to Althorpe Island, south of Yorke Peninsula. He took his fishing rod, because he was not at all sure he'd go into the water. He was having a fine time with the rod and reel, pulling in fish, when a school of kingfish swam eight feet below the boat. Everyone immediately prepared to go in.

"I don't remember making a decision at all," Rodney recalled. "When I jumped into the water, it hit me that I was going in."

The boat crew put the dinghy in the water and rowed off to a nearby island. The three divers went into the school of kingfish and spread out. He was diving between 30 to 40 feet and could see the bottom below him at 50 feet. Then, he saw a shark.

"All of a sudden, off the bottom, straight at me like a rocket, was this big shark," Rodney said. "I looked at my gun and thought what a piddling little thing it was. The shark took off and I went to the surface, screaming like a madman. I swam toward the boat, but there was nobody aboard because they had left in the dinghy. I couldn't pull myself out because my arms were still weak."

He swam back to the others and told them about the shark, which he estimated was eight to nine feet long. "Oh, yeah?" they said. "What sort of shark?" They weren't immediately concerned. The three of them swam together, keeping two guns loaded for the shark and one to use on the kingfish if they came back through. "Well," said Rodney, with a laugh. "I wasn't going to spear any damned fish! I was going to watch out for the shark!"

By the end of the day, he had speared a 65-pound grouper, the biggest catch of the day. He'd also speared the biggest psychological hurdle he'd have to face in his return to the sea. He felt strongly that if he'd been able to pull himself out of the water that day, he never would have gone back to diving.

"I would have been a bricklayer, not a diver," Rodney said. "I realized right then and there that you have to live with sharks as they are. You can't go around being afraid of them without knowing why. I analyzed it quite a lot and worked it out."

He began to dive more and more, until he became a commercial abalone diver, an occupation which put him in the territory of the great white shark day in and day out. In over 5,000 hours of abalone diving, Rodney saw all kinds of sharks. He knows about the great white in particular, because he set himself to understand the behavior of that animal. Rodney's side benefit from choosing that course of action is his shark business. Anytime anyone needs a great white shark for a film or adventure travel thrill, Rodney Fox is the one they call.

He enjoys taking people out to see the great white sharks, and he does it more often than anyone. Once a year an exclusive expedition is organized by a San Francisco travel agency that puts people in shark cages off the South Australian coast with Rodney Fox. It is the ultimate underwater adventure, the undersea equivalent of the big game safari.

Rodney chums the water with buckets of fish guts, tuna, horsemeat and blood, while everyone prepares to dive. Usually a great white shark will swim in to give the divers a thrill they've never had before. With any luck at all, the great whites that come will behave ferociously, attacking the cages, biting the rudder of the boat, biting the propeller, the zincs, anything metal. The animal is maniacal and is just what the divers have paid thousands of dollars to come across the world to see.

When one sees a great white shark in action, watches it in a frenzy as its ragged teeth alternately tear off hunks of horsemeat, or gnaw at the bars that separate it from the humans, one is stunned at the force of the enormous beast. One is also stunned to consider Rodney Fox still wanting to be around them. Almost everyone who sees a great white shark from the inside of one of Rodney's shark cages reacts the same way—with incredulity. That's how it was with the crew of *Jaws,* with the divers of the film *Blue Water–White Death,* with the crew of the ABC-television documentary *Mysteries of the Sea,* and with the British and Japanese filmmakers who came to Rodney for help. It is the same way with those who pay thousands of dollars to see the sharks with Rodney.

Rodney enjoys seeing people having a good time. While he likes to heighten their sense of amazement on these trips with his stories, he does not like to see unjust fear when it comes to sharks. He tells people that sharks should be treated with respect, that the sea is their world, but that not too much should be made of sharks. Sharks don't roam around, looking for people to attack, he says. If a man gets bitten, it's usually a case of mistaken identity.

"I try to tell the truth about sharks," Rodney said. "To allow fear of them to keep you from the sea is to miss out on one of the greatest things in life."

I looked at him. The scar on his right arm is invisible, his right hand fully functional, everything about him normal. The only souvenir of his great white encounter is the permanent jaw-shaped scar embedded in his left side, now masked in Mt. Gambier by a flowered sport shirt.

There had to be more, I thought. Here was a man who had lived through something not possible to live through. There had to be a residual effect somewhere, something more than just a scar. Maybe there were nightmares.

"Come to think of it," Rodney said, "I guess there is one thing. It usually happens at a party!" He began to rub a spot just below his rib cage. "Halfway through the evening with friends, I might get carried away. If I start laughing, I'll get a ball, or a cramp, just about here. It's where a bit of muscle is attached to the skin and I have to get up and rub it."

As I consider Rodney's story now, I think he must have decided deep inside himself that there were no setbacks to keep worrying about. One thing is certain: Rodney Fox may have been in the wrong place at the wrong time, but his attitude provoked him to create success from disaster.

**Suggested Reading**

Richard Ellis, *The Book of Sharks* (Grosset & Dunlap: New York, 1976).

## Chapter 11

Jack McKenney

# Devil's Hole

*Never say die.*

— *Dickens*

B eware of Wild Dogs and Buckshot!
   I looked at the sign and then I looked at my friend Jack. How we were going to proceed from this point was entirely up to him. Out in a remote corner of the Amargosa Desert of Nevada, one didn't just drive into a place that had a sign like that without giving it a little thought. On the other hand, we were lost, had almost torn the car apart on wretched roads, and even though it was almost dark, it was a sweltering 100° in the shade. This was the first hint of civilization we had seen in a while.

We were looking for Devil's Hole, an enormous, water-filled earthquake fault that is part of the Death Valley National Monument. We figured something like Devil's Hole would be easy to pick out in the parched, flat landscape, but we had figured wrong. After zig-zagging the desert for a good part of the afternoon, our good dispositions were evaporating with the outside heat.

At the very bottom of our increasing uneasiness was the fact that once we found Devil's Hole we weren't sure what we would be able to do with it. We had tried for weeks to get permission to dive and photograph it, but National Park Service restrictions were severe. A number of divers had died in the hole, and the cave was also the only home in the world for the endangered Devil's Hole pupfish. Just as the snail darter had halted the megamillion dollar construction of a dam

113

in Tennessee, the Devil's Hole pupfish had stopped the pumping of water from underneath the Amargosa Desert.

It was all a heated matter and, in the middle of the fire, I had convinced a major magazine that a story on Devil's Hole would be rather good. The magazine had given us a go-ahead, depending upon the pictures we could get. The National Park Service, however, didn't want unnecessary people stepping on the pupfish, and that was that. The Park Service had given me permission to make one dive, as a safety diver for the scientist who counted the fish every month. I had convinced Jack to go with me to Death Valley to see what photos we could scare up. There were other springs and sinkholes which could be part of the story. Now we couldn't find the springs and sinkholes, nor Devil's Hole itself.

Jack McKenney is an old friend of mine with whom I'd worked on other underwater assignments. I wondered what he was thinking now as he looked at the wild dogs and buckshot salutation.

"What the heck," said Jack. "Let's give it a try."

I was relieved to hear that Jack's sense of adventure was far from dead.

We drove into the fenced area toward a tin shack set in the middle of a large collection of rusted bedsprings, old appliances, benches, kitchen sinks, machinery and other odds and ends. The only thing missing from this permanent swap meet was a rusted-out car on its axles, a sight quite common in the desert.

Immediately two big dogs charged at the car, barking and snarling, one at each door. "Nice doggy," said Jack. That was an enormous amount of optimism, the type Daniel must have had when he faced the lions that were supposed to eat him.

A man emerged from the tin house (without a gun). He didn't seem belligerent, and he called off the dogs.

"We're lost," Jack called out. "Could you tell us where Devil's Hole is?"

"Shore!" said the man. "Why don't you come in and sit a bit?"

This wasn't buckshot by any means. We proceeded to get out of our car, only to find that the wild dogs jumped up on us like big puppies.

"Down, boy!" yelled the man. He extended his hand to us. "Name's Rex," he said.

Jack and I introduced ourselves and told him what we were doing. "What do you know?" Rex said, "Follow me."

He led us over to an area of his yard which was fenced in by the circular ends of enormous wooden spools, and pointed off in the distance. "See that mountain over there?" he asked. "The very last one of that bunch?"

We said that we did.

"See that dark spot? Near the base of it?"

114

Photo by Hillary Hauser

Rex Schneehagen's house (left) sits well protected from the casually curious passerby (above).

We made out the dark spot.

"That's Devil's Hole."

He drew a map for us in the dirt and told us how to get there. "You know," he said, standing up, "there's a hole right here, next door to me. A big one. Used to be bottomless until one of them atomic bomb tests caved the thing in."

Jack and I looked at each other.

"It's deep, you can dive in it," he continued. "Sand is boiling up all the time."

"We'd like to see it," I said. "Could we?"

"Shore!" said Rex. He gave us directions on how to get there through his property. "Leave the gate down when you come back through," he said. "So that the horses can get back in."

We went immediately to look at Rex's spring. It was exactly what we had been looking for. It was 30 feet deep and the sand was boiling up at the bottom as he had said it did, like bubbling lava. Contrary to Rex's imaginative tale, the pool hadn't really been caved in by a bomb blast. Instead, it was a perfect example of the geologic phenomenon of the desert sinkhole, where water dissolves the bottom of the pool as it pushes up from an underground water supply. Our photographs would show perfectly this vital link in the desert water system.

We were really happy right then and drove back to thank Rex. He was in his tin house when we arrived, wrestling with some frozen orange juice cans on top

*Photo by Jack McKenney*

*Death Valley Desert (right) and the barbed wire enclosure around Devil's Hole (below).*

*Photo by Jack McKenney*

of his wood-burning stove. "Can't get enough darn cans together to organize this," he complained. He turned to a cupboard over a crude wooden table and fished around for what I thought would be something to organize the orange juice. Instead he pulled out a cereal bowl, filled it with cat food and set it on the floor. A gray kitten materialized out of nowhere and began to eat. Rex went back to his orange juice project. Watching over him from the wall was Christ, who looked out over the one-room desert cabin in a handsomely framed print of The Last Supper.

I asked Rex his last name.

"Just start spelling," he answered. I got out my pen. "S-c-h-n-e-e-h-a-g-e-n," he spelled.

"Schneehagen?" I asked. "What nationality is that?"

"American," said Rex.

Jack and I were in the highest of spirits as we drove toward our lodgings in Furnace Creek. We now knew where Devil's Hole was and Rex Schneehagen was a gold mine. The next day we'd be able to dive and photograph in Rex's spring. We'd get the magazine assignment for sure. It was all a stroke of luck.

Then it hit us. Adventure was really the thin line between boom or bust. We'd both felt completely helpless five minutes before we'd met Rex Schneehagen, and now we felt grand. We realized, too, that if everything had been set up for us without the risk of failure, we would have had the security of knowing exactly what we were doing, but none of the thrill of chance. Chance is the very stuff adventure is made of. We might have fallen flat on our faces, but since it looked as if we might make it, the sense of victory seemed ever so much sweeter. We'd done it on our own, made our own discovery, broken our own trail. Though others had probably done it a thousand times before, it made no difference; we had done it all ourselves.

I had heard about Devil's Hole just after I returned from exploring the freshwater caves of South Australia. I was sitting around the living room with my friends Chris and Hadda Swann one evening, telling them about the caves. I told them about diving in the middle of a sheep pasture, underneath a forest and a road, and about what it felt like to crawl and swim around darkened, flooded passageways and rooms with lights and lines. Chris, who is British, jumped up with an "Aye Saye!" and ran to get something from another room. He came back with an old film festival program describing Merl Dobry's documentary on Devil's Hole. In the program was a diagram of Devil's Hole, showing what was underground and underwater, describing what the hole was about and how it had been formed. I had heard of Devil's Hole because of the pupfish issue, which had been U.S. news, but I had never imagined that it would be so big, deep and

complicated. From the diagram I could see there were multitudinous passageways that angled off the main shaft. A narrow slot edged to one side of the main shaft and opened into a giant air-filled room underneath the mountain. Below a narrow passageway that descended to 160 feet was an enormous chamber of water that continued to at least 260 feet. No one had bottomed the hole, so its exact depth was unknown.

From the diagram and description, Devil's Hole appeared to be more exciting than any of the holes we'd dived in Australia. In looking at all of this material, I found myself becoming a little excited and curious.

The desert of Death Valley is geology in action, a silent, eternal kiln where panoramic rocks are fired day after day in sun that never quits. It is a harsh, untamed land that bears names like Furnace Creek, Desolate Canyon, Badwater, Dante's View, Hell's Gate, and Ash Meadows—home of Devil's Hole. The land seems fluid still, with its boiling, bubbling, moving, cracking and faulting earth now frozen in time. Mountains have spilled their volcanic ooze down bumpy canyons in roller-coaster paths of heated chocolate bordered by vanilla-colored pumice and sand. Dark rivers of black ash snake through mounds of caked mustard clay. Sharp, jagged crags, once buried deep in granite, shoot upward in violent explosions that are frozen in midair. The land is untouched by man because it is so untouchable. The only evidences of his being there are the occasional giant anthills where he has dug for minerals. Zeolite, the soft green

*Photo by Jack McKenney*

*Photo by Jack McKenney*

*A topside view of Big Spring (opposite page). Hillary Hauser explores the underground tunnels and limestone walls of Devil's Hole (left and above).*

moonlike rock used to filter water, is piled up beside the roads. Old scars in the sides of mountains reveal abandoned gold or silver mines. But it is borax, the "white gold" of the desert, that is important here. Borax gave Death Valley its twenty-mule-team history.

It was hard to imagine that at one time the dry, salt-encrusted desert on which we stood was a fertile, green, freshwater land of lakes and rivers. It was even harder to imagine that such an enormous amount of fresh, pure water was now underground, hidden from sight.

The geologic history of Death Valley tells us how this water system came to be. In late Precambrian and Early Cambrian time, Death Valley was beneath the sea, as much of the world was. The shoreline, it is estimated, lay to the east near modern Las Vegas. By the Middle Cambrian to Permian time (550 million years ago), the skeletal carcasses of innumerable generations of corals, shellfish and other sea animals had created an enormous mass of lime and sand. This mass then consolidated into a limestone and dolomite layer more than two miles thick in some areas, perhaps only tens of feet in others.

In Mesozoic time (225–65 million years ago), a chain of volcanoes arose along the present Sierra Nevadas, and the sea withdrew. The limestoned Death Valley region became a highland.

Limestone is porous, and the rainfall from a big area of Nevada northeast of Ash Meadows and Death Valley collected underground, forming a major water table. As it ran in the direction of Ash Meadows, this water dissolved the limestone. In some areas where it collected and pooled, it ate upward through the limestone until the surface land collapsed downward, creating the sinkhole. This was the same geologic process that had created the sinkholes in South Australia.

Devil's Hole, on the other hand, is a flooded earthquake fault, formed by one of the earthquake or faulting actions of the Mesozoic period. Extending into the earth from the base of an unnamed mountain in the Amargosa Desert, it filled with the water that permeated the rest of the underground area. In Devil's Hole, the water began to eat away at the limestone fissures, enlarging the caverns and creating new passageways, new tunnels and chambers.

The bottom of Rex Schneehagen's spring in Ash Meadows, officially called Big Spring, was disintegrating before our eyes and, during some geologic time down the road, the bottom of that spring would collapse, perhaps opening up into some enormous chamber like that of Devil's Hole. Or, perhaps it would only be a shallow pool or underground river. One needs X-ray eyes to see what is underneath that bubbling sand pile.

At 8:00 a.m. the next morning, Jack and I arrived at Devil's Hole.

It looked like a prison camp sunk into one side of a volcanic mountain. Giant coils of barbed wire tangled with the metal mesh of a high, impenetrable fence to seal off the confining pit from the outside world. At one end was a heavy gate, sealed shut with a massive chain and padlock. Just inside the gate was a steep rock cliff, bridged by a wooden ladder propped against its uppermost ledge. A rock slope descended the rest of the way to the bottom of the cavern, where a rectangular trough of water emerged from underneath the mountain. That trough of water was bottomless, a flooded earthquake fault.

At 8:30 Jim Deacon arrived. So did Pete Sanchez from the National Park Service, Bob Yoder from the U.S. Fish and Wildlife Service, and a representative from the Bureau of Land Management. It was all serious business. Pete Sanchez, who'd been with the Park Service in Death Valley for 12 years, sat with me on a rock, and in casual conversation I asked him if he had ever found anything valuable while poking around in the desert sands.

"Sure!" he said.

"Like agates?" I asked.

"No!" he answered emphatically. "Nothing monetary. Only plants and animals. Things other people might not think valuable, things you can't put a price on. But to me those things are valuable."

Pete Sanchez was not only resource management specialist with the Park

*Photo by Jack McKenney*

*Photo by Jack McKenney*

*The clear water of Big Spring allows a diver to swim easily to the bottom and watch the sands "bubble".*

Service, he was head of the Desert Pupfish Council. It was obvious to me that he was the best possible choice for both jobs.

Jim Deacon prepared for the morning dive. He laid down a narrow bridge of boards over the shallow shelf of bright green algae where the pupfish live, and then we geared up. There would be three of us on the dive—Jim, me, and Park Service safety diver Bob Todd.

As I tight-roped across the narrow boards in my heavy diving gear, I looked down at the tiny fishes, each one of them no bigger than a minnow. They swam leisurely around their shelf, picking at algae, oblivious to the human *sturm und drang* above them. They didn't know about the badges or the barbed wire. Most likely they were oblivious to the fact that there were so few of their numbers left in the world. They were tiny little fishes under enormous lock and key.

I carefully put one foot on the very edge of the shelf and lowered myself backward into a drop-off of clear, blue water. As I waited for the others, I looked down through my facemask and could see the first ledge below me at 30 feet. Swimming in the 92° water was like swimming in nothing. It was so clear that visibility might have been 300 feet. It was like soaring in air, the closest thing to flying I'd every known.

121

As the three of us sank through that giant, water-filled crack in the earth—so deep it hadn't been bottomed—I was reminded of how I felt during our exploration of the Australian sinkholes. The feeling of anticipation, wonder and excitement at swimming into a dark underground, underwater cave was just as strong now as it had been then.

The sides of the main shaft of Devil's Hole consist of white limestone, laid down 550 million years ago and chiseled over the years by water into smooth slopes on either side. Rust-colored organic material on top of the elevated ridges of stone created an ethereal, other-worldly effect. At 60 feet, I turned and looked up toward the surface. The bright blue of the shallow water at the surface illuminated the main shaft and silhouetted the sloping wall on the right side. From where I hovered, I could see people standing around on the rocks above, almost as clearly as if there had been no water between us. Just as distinct was the long, rectangular lamp which hung over the water, positioned over the pupfish shelf and turned on when algae production needs a boost. Another shaft of light beamed down from behind a rock in back of the main entrance. The slope of limestone leading up to it created a narrow ledge against the ceiling of the cave.

I turned again toward the bottom and the three of us switched on our lights. We sank to 90 feet where an enormous flat stone called Anvil Rock signalled the deepest part of our dive. This stone, shaped like an enormous anvil and obviously shaken loose from above, marks the deepest spot where the pupfish wander from their shallow shelf. Jim started counting at this point while I beamed my underwater light down beyond Anvil Rock to see what I could see. I knew that below Anvil Rock was the narrow funnel that went to 160 feet and the deeper chamber. Merl Dobry had explored this chamber. The area had invited trouble in the past. Nitrogen narcosis had robbed at least one diver of judgment and common sense here. It was in this chamber that two divers had disappeared years before, and their bodies were never recovered. One needed good lights and a safety line system to explore Devil's Hole.

The most exciting area of Devil's Hole Merl had described was Brown's Room. This huge, air-filled, underground chamber is accessible only through a narrow slit that angles off to the left of Anvil Rock. Merl had talked about the squeeze in getting past the opening, about the enormous, cathedral-like room that opens into an air-filled chamber beneath the mountain.

While poking around Anvil Rock, I saw a line, tied permanently around a rock, angling up through the narrow passageway that leads to Brown's Room.

I looked at the other two. Jim was counting fish at about 60 feet and Bob was watching him count. I wasn't going to see Brown's Room on this dive, so I swam up and joined the others.

Later, over pizza at a mid-desert saloon near the California-Nevada border, Jim explained that the pupfish had been stranded in Devil's Hole 20,000 years ago, when the freshwater system of the desert began to dry up and recede. Because Devil's Hole was one of the higher habitats, these creatures were the first to be stranded, the first of the desert pupfishes to evolve into a separate, distinct species.

The continuing desiccation of the area resulted in similar isolation and consequent reduced survival odds for other populations of desert pupfish. The Tecopa and Shoshone pupfish are extinct already, and the Warm Springs pupfish are endangered now. Other desert pupfish in the area, such as those in Crystal Spring, are all right for the moment, said Deacon, because at that desert level, the water is still flowing between the springs and ponds where the fish live and propagate.

All pupfish species have tolerated periodic difficult living conditions, usually associated with summer heat. When the sun is hot, their habitats dry up. Some pupfish survive parched summers in homes the size of a teacup. When water evaporates in these limited living quarters, salinity levels increase. The desert pupfish, Jim said, is one of the few fish in the world that can tolerate such concentrations of salt. The fish also withstands the freezing temperatures of winter and a host of other difficulties, which include competitive foreign species of fish and crayfish that fight the pupfish for food and space.

The irony is that the adaptable little fish probably cannot withstand what human beings want to do to it. Yet another battle was brewing in Ash Meadows over water rights at the very moment Jack and I were there. The pupfish was again threatened by a land development scheme which planned to turn 13,000 acres of Ash Meadows into a recreational-housing-golf course development. It was going to be a war for water, and again, the Devil's Hole pupfish were going to be under the gun.

While we sat in the mid-desert saloon, Jack played devil's advocate and put forth the loaded question to Jim. "Why save the pupfish?" he asked.

Jim Deacon is one of those rare individuals whose work is serious, but who doesn't take himself seriously. He answered the question as if he had answered it many times, yet he was just as interested in the concept of what he was saying as if he'd thought about it for the first time.

"Two ways of looking at that question," he said. "One, if you value the earth, then you must also value the way it functions. Extinction of a species is a momentous event, because it removes one irreplaceable role in the functioning of the earth. Man is causing extinctions at an alarming rate. If the process continues, the resulting instabilities will affect the way the world works, making it less reliable for humans, as well as for other populations of animals.

"The other thing," he continued, "is that every living species represents a complex living system—a library of information. If man's uniqueness is his ability to know, then we have to protect that library of knowledge, which in this case is a live pupfish."

Deacon sat back and thought. "Actually, do you know what the best answer is?" he said. "It's because they're here. That's all the reason you need."

Jack and I later went to dive in Crystal Spring, fed by Devil's Hole over two miles away. When I free-dived to the bottom of the spring, I felt the enormous rush of water coming in from the bottom, almost 4,000 gallons per minute. At the height of the controversial pumping of the underground water supply of the desert, the water pressure in Crystal Spring had declined to 1,670 gallons per minute, less than half its normal capacity.

Crystal Spring is one of the bigger holes in the area. The smaller pools, under such abuse, would literally dry up, never to return, even if the pumping were stopped. Once dry, always dry—that's how it works. The main flow of water in Crystal Spring comes in at its deepest part, in 30 feet of water. As we swam around the other areas of the spring, we saw the water pushing in from beneath the limestone bed, creating little circles of bubbling sands where the pupfish liked to congregate. It was as if they enjoyed the massage they got from the miniature water jets, or perhaps there was an oxygenation of the water they took advantage of.

There is plenty of water in Crystal Spring. There also seems to be an infinite amount of it in Devil's Hole and in the entire network of the desert's underground passageways. However, what happens in one spot affects another almost immediately. The system is fragile, temperamental. The water is the arterial life blood which cannot be siphoned lest the veins collapse.

We dived a number of the desert sinkholes, but in my mind I could still see Brown's Room and the permanent safety line tied around the rock leading up to it.

Some weeks later, Jack and I returned to Devil's Hole.

We carefully laid down the narrow bridge of boards over the shallow shelf where the pupfish lived and we geared up quickly. We stepped on the very edge of the shelf and lowered ourselves backward into the flooded drop-off. With our powerful underwater lights switched on, we swam quickly to the first ledge below, at 30 feet. Even in the dark, the water was warm and clear. We sank down through the main shaft until we were at Anvil Rock, at 90 feet. Again, I saw the permanent safety line and pointed it out to Jack. We quickly went for the line.

With our lights picking the way through the narrow, dark crack, I followed

Jack along the safety line, which I held in my left hand. The back of my tank scraped the limestone wall overhead as I pulled myself along on my stomach through the narrow opening. When we cleared the opening, we were at the bottom of the cavern I'd been told about. Our lights illuminated the entire, flooded room. Enormous limestone walls rose up from 80 feet and conglomerates of granite jutted through the whiteness of the limestone to create a submerged work of art. The white line led upward through the dark cavern.

Following the line, we rose up through the clear, transparent water. It was still as warm as at the entrance of the main shaft, because this water is heated by the depths of earth rather than by sunlight.

The reflection of my light hit the surface of the water, becoming silver as mercury against the bright white walls. Because of the clarity of the water, it was almost impossible to tell the depth in which we swam. We had moved from 90 feet to the surface in a matter of minutes.

When we broke through to air, I was completely stunned by what I saw. The cavern of Brown's Room is enormous, probably 50 feet from the surface of the water to the ceiling. About ten feet above us, a dry passageway led off into a dark crack, another passageway. According to the diagram of Devil's Hole, that dark crack turned down again into yet another water-filled chamber. The walls of the main chamber were rusty brown and ancient. We were completely sealed off from the outside world, underneath a mountain in a Nevada desert. It was like a scene from *The Phantom of the Opera.*

We pulled our regulators out of our mouths and took a taste of the air. It was musty and we didn't know the quality of it, so we immediately switched back to our regulators. I turned off my light, Jack turned off his. Instantly, the room became pitch black. That was enough. We turned our lights on again and headed down, free-falling along the safety line until we came to the narrow crack that led us back to the main shaft. We squeezed through the passage, inching our way along on our bellies like snakes, and we came out at Anvil Rock. Together, we rose up through the main shaft until we were back at the first ledge at 30 feet. Here, we stopped to have a long, close look at the tiny fishes.

The Devil's Hole pupfishes are living in a palace fit for the king of fishes—in the Eighth Wonder of the World.

*Chapter 12*

*Carleton Ray*

# Carleton Ray:
# Marine Revolutionary

*For the things we have to learn*
*before we can do them,*
*we learn by doing them.*

— *Aristotle*

———

In the winter of 1969, a CBS television crew filmed a one-hour documentary about regions of the world most of us may never see—the Arctic and Antarctic. Cameras focused on G. Carleton Ray, noted marine ecologist who has made many expeditions to both regions. The film was *The Frozen World of Seals and Walruses.*

Carleton Ray was the first to take a detailed look at marine mammals underwater in the Antarctic. He made his first dives there in 1963, at a time no one had heard of diving equipment that would shield divers from bitter ice and cold. Inventions usually always follow necessity. As the polar regions of the world began to catch the scientific eye, diving equipment for extremely cold environments began to emerge.

Carleton organized many such polar expeditions in those days. As often as three times a year he traveled to the Arctic to gain firsthand knowledge of seals, whales and walruses. I had seen photographs of him in an ordinary black wetsuit, submerged at the surface amid giant blocks of glaring white ice, peeking nose-to-nose at a Weddell seal through his facemask, with steam rising all around.

In 1971 I was at Boston University, delivering an impassioned lecture at a diving convention about the perilous plight of porpoises, which were being killed by the thousands in the nets of tuna fishermen. I was advocating a congressional campaign to outlaw such nets.

Afterward, a man I'd never met stepped forward out of the audience and introduced himself as Carleton Ray. He asked if I had time for a little talk.

I felt honored by this invitation, because I knew who he was and because I had no idea what he was about to tell me. I think I talked first, carrying on about how I had become familiar with his work when I started writing a monthly feature on marine fishes for *Skin Diver Magazine.* I relied heavily on scientific literature and fish books such as his *Underwater Guide to Marine Life,* which he had published in 1956 with marine author and photographer Elgin Ciampi.

Carleton listened patiently, then carefully explained what was wrong with my argument about the porpoises. Something needed to be done about the nets, he said, but by banning them before an alternative technique was developed, tuna fishermen would be forced to fish outside U.S. waters, where there were no restrictions whatsoever on porpoise kills. If this happened, more porpoises might be killed than ever before.

To really help the porpoises, he said, I might want to consider another piece of legislation that required an escape door in the nets and called for additional studies to alleviate the problem. He said an alliance, not an adversarial relationship, should be established with the fishermen. The environmental awakenings of the time were good, he said, but one had to consider the whole picture in order to be effective.

I'll never forget Carleton's kindness in setting me straight, and we became longtime friends after that. Over the years, he has visited me in California, and we have dived underneath oil platforms in the Santa Barbara Channel.

In 1978 Carleton came through Los Angeles on his way to Alaska and Japan, and arrangements were made for me to interview him for *Skin Diver*. At the last minute, Jack McKenney, editor of the magazine, had to cancel his photographing of the interview. He told me I could shoot the photographs myself, although the only camera I owned was a Nikonos, an underwater camera. Take Carleton Ray outside, Jack said. Use such and such settings, shoot with available light, and take lots of pictures.

As our interview progressed, it began to rain, and it was still raining when I asked Carleton to step outside for a picture. He really couldn't believe it when I pulled out my underwater camera. He stepped out into the rain and sat willingly under a banana tree that dripped water on his head. He even smiled nicely as I shot picture after picture. That is the way Carleton is: game for anything. Of course, I'm sure that having made numerous dives in the Arctic and Antarctic, he'd certainly seen worse weather.

Carleton made his first dive in 1953 in Bermuda with Elgin Ciampi, a marine life photographer he'd met at Columbia University. They used scuba gear they had built themselves. The next year the two came up with the idea of setting aside underwater parks for nonspearfishing divers and underwater photographers. This was during a time everyone believed scuba diving was a great way to catch lots of underwater game, long before anyone had thought seriously of ocean conservation. However, people gained interest in the marine park idea. In 1958 Carleton and Ilia A. Tolstoy headed an expedition to the Exuma Cays, Bahamas, where they proposed the first land-and-sea park in the world. Consequently, the Bahamas National Trust was formed.

At the time, Carleton was assistant to the director of the New York Aquarium, with degrees in zoology from Yale and Columbia under his arm. He was 30 years old. He went to Seattle in 1962, where the First World Conference of National Parks was under way, and with Sir Peter Scott of England drafted Resolution No. 15, which called for the development of underwater marine parks. In subsequent years, he helped to define marine priorities and identified the critical marine habitats of the world, publishing dozens of papers on their conservation.

He coined the term "Marine Revolution", which describes human dependency on the ocean and implies a major change in the way man regards (and exploits) the sea. He has predicted that the Marine Revolution will take its place beside the Agricultural and Industrial Revolutions in altering basic human behavior on the planet. Critical marine habitats and global conservation issues are Carleton's primary work, an expansive field that began with his early studies of marine mammals.

In his work, Carleton has dived in every ocean of the world, but the Arctic has been his favorite laboratory. Through a mixture of chance and luck, he became involved in marine-oriented research. When a graduate student finishes his studies, Carleton said, he really doesn't know where his exact future will lie, but chance and luck often open doors that need to be opened.

"The great Fairfield Osborn offered me a job with the New York Zoological Society's Aquarium because I'd done a lot of diving and I had thoughts on marine conservation," Carleton said. "One day, a couple of walruses came to the aquarium, sent by a collector from Alaska, and they arrived dead. That made me mad. I thought, a bit cockily, that I could ship walruses better than that. My boss, Christopher Coates, said, 'Okay, you try it,' and that's how I got into marine mammals."

He had many failures, but eventually some of the walruses he brought back from Alaska became "the first to survive the trip and grow normally." Soon after, this type of relocation became almost commonplace. The animals, however, still do not thrive easily in a captive environment.

Carleton began his well-known studies of Arctic mammals because of the challenge they presented to him.

"I went up there and brought the animals back and had a hell of a time keeping them alive," he said. "I spent a lot of time devising diets—artificial diets—and in the process had a lot of tragedies."

Because he wanted to know more, Carleton started diving in Antarctica in 1963.

129

"For a long time, people had studied marine mammals from the surface, where we could see them like we see an iceberg, about 10 percent. But this new business of diving gave us the ability to go underwater and be like seals, so to speak. In Antarctica, we dived and dived and found out a lot of things that we couldn't have found out at the surface."

Because dry suits hadn't been invented, it was difficult for him to stay submerged for long in the icy waters. So, he began to think of other techniques for looking at these amphibious animals.

In 1964 he installed an underwater habitat in the Antarctic. He called it the *Sub-Ice Observation Chamber.* Unlike Joe MacInnis's later *Sub-Igloo,* Carleton's habitat didn't require diver entry. A ladder ran down a long tube from the surface. The scientists could climb down the tube, look at seals from the windows of the chamber and stay dry. Carleton described it as an upside-down thing that looked like a sparbuoy, anchored under the ice rather than positioned on the ocean bottom.

Walruses took top priority in his studies, because they appeared to be important environmental indicators.

"Ice dynamics are directly related to weather dynamics of the whole northern hemisphere," Carleton said. "Walruses move with the ice, and we're developing tools to watch what's going on, to monitor walruses with remote sensing devices. The walrus could be an important indicator of Arctic pollution, which is something we have to watch, especially now that we're going for oil and gas up there. The walrus feeds on the bottom. If anything happens to bottom organisms, if benthic productivity is altered in any way, the walrus population may let us know."

Marine mammals also gave the scientists an insight into diving physiology.

"They do the same things we do basically, but to a greater extent," Carleton said. "They have a few valves and other adaptations that we don't have and they have stiffer bronchioles in their lungs and that kind of thing. Actually these are but modifications on the basic mammalian scheme which we share. In the course of evolution, marine mammals have modified this system into the finest diving machine that we know among mammals."

When marine mammals dive, they do what surgeons call a heart-brain preparation. That is, the circulation to all parts of their bodies, except the heart and brain, slows to a trickle. The red blood cell count of marine mammals is much higher than in humans, and they have more myoglobin ("which is like hemoglobin, only in the muscle"). Marine mammals are able to tolerate more carbon dioxide when diving than humans are.

"The world champion diving times as far as we know are those of marine mammals," Carleton said.

Courtesy of Carleton Ray

*Carleton Ray with Weddell seal.*

Weddell seals have been recorded to dive for over an hour to depths of about 2,000 feet. Sperm whales dive well over a mile and can stay underwater over an hour. Although both species could probably double these diving times, animals usually don't push to their full potential.

Carleton said he wouldn't predict the value of applying marine mammal research to humans, and he questioned the advisability of building a *Homo aquaticus* "as some have suggested."

"The practicality of the study of marine mammals is not really all that matters. Life is enriched by both art and science; the two are very close. The purpose of studying is really to achieve a basic understanding of our earth-sea home."

In assessing the conditions of the oceans, Carleton takes a realistic approach to the problems of pollution. He disagrees with statements that the oceans are dying.

"That is the opposite of 'The oceans are too big to pollute,'" he said. "Both are wrong. The oceans *aren't* dying. The earth's not dying. There is going to be life here a long, long time. But what is happening involves a breakdown of ecosystems. In using the word ecosystem, few people bother to define what that is. You are a system; a cell is a system. But if you take all the living things and the

131

*Carleton Ray (far left) with divers on the ice.*

nonliving things in an environment, the biotic things and the abiotic things, and if they interact as a more or less integrated unit that processes energy and materials, it's an ecosystem. Sure, there are changes, fluctuations. A system can lose its integrity and can be destroyed when it no longer can sustain itself. There may still be productivity, more life than ever before, but it may be the sort of life you don't want and the whole system loses its character.

"Take, for an example, your own body. You can cut your arms and your legs off, you can cut a lot of things off, and you still may live. But there are a lot of things you can't do anymore. You can't run and throw and kick. Your ability to survive is very depleted. The least little thing that comes along may clobber a blind man, whereas somebody who can see could get out of the way. So, what do we mean by the death of the oceans? We don't mean they are dying. We mean their systems are breaking down. It behooves those who are saying the oceans are dying to be specific, to be very specific."

Carleton estimated that the total length of all the coastlines of the world, including the Arctic and Antarctic, when divided by the number of people on earth, would allow about 13 centimeters of coastline for each person.

"That's not much," he said. "In fact, you couldn't stand side by side, because most people are wider than 13 centimeters. Take that, and then consider the fact that man has always gone to protected coves and harbors to develop cities, the estuarine places like Baltimore Harbor, Los Angeles, and Long Beach harbors, San Francisco Bay—all these nice protected places which are, or were, among the richest places for living resources in the world. So, the richest places in the world are also the most populated and are subject to man's greatest perturbations. This leads to the extremely alarming fact that, while he's increasing his numbers, man is also decreasing the coastal capacity to provide biological living materials for him, since estuarine places are nursery grounds to most forms of ocean life.

"But even these areas are not dying. In fact, some are getting richer. But they're getting richer in things you don't want to eat. Many areas are getting to be what is called eutrophic. What happens in such areas where more nutrients are added is more oxygen depletion, and you get a vicious cycle of events which overenriches the coastal zone and makes life for some creatures impossible. With all these lovely things in mind, it's unthinkable that in man's quest for more space, there is an increase in coastal development. There are even those who have come along with ideas for man-made offshore city islands and all sorts of crazy stuff."

Carleton explained that offshore islands are built by dredging or dumping spoils, which increases siltation and smothers living things. Increased siltation, he said, is one of the most deadly things for a benthic community.

133

"There are two big problems with this," he said. "First, it's very damaging to the life of the sea in general, because over two-thirds of all the fish in the ocean depend upon the coastal zone for breeding or other life functions. The other is economic. Living resources are not so great a short-term economic value as nonliving ones, even though over the long term they are infinitely more valuable, as they are renewable. Let's be frank about it—coastal development is mostly a money-making proposition, a sacrifice of nonrenewable resources and values for short-range economic benefits."

Coral reefs need to be protected, too, from unrestricted diving.

"It's what we call carrying capacity," Carleton said. "Just like a field can hold just so many cows, so a reef can hold just so many divers without damage. It's not sufficient to protect a reef from spearfishing and the collecting of corals, seafans and shells. The very presence of continuous, high-intensity use disturbs fish and corals, causes some breakage of delicate coral structures."

Management plans have to be developed so that some reefs will have "diver relief" from time to time. Many terrestrial parks have had to do this, he said, adding that he saw no reason for similar development of ocean management plans.

"If the restraint costs us more, so be it. We save in the end. Right now we are talking about not wrecking the ocean, but we're exploiting it haphazardly. We've got to understand the ecosystems of the ocean and put our knowledge to work."

Echoing the theme of our visit in Boston in 1971, Carleton said the future of the planet has to lie in a scientific plan that includes the whole picture—including man's use of it. Special-interest groups battling each other over the use of a certain space or species doesn't work, he said, because "the basic problem" is still there.

The basic problem is the doubling of the Earth's population, a factor that must be considered in every scientific plan for the planet. For example, it is useless to save whales only by ceasing to kill them. The ocean in which the whales swim must be kept unpolluted as well. Since oceans are not delineated by boundaries, the pollution problem is not the problem of one country, but of every country.

"Boundaries are wrong," Carleton said. "It's ecological nonsense. You have to get the big global picture. What you learn in one place can apply to another. We don't exist separately. What goes on in Saudi Arabia can affect Prudhoe Bay."

Since large populations are a fact of life, scientists can no longer exclude the activities of man in outlining a global picture. Man has to be seen as part of the plan, too. Some of the greatest populations live along the richest coastal areas, and man uses the sea.

134

"Humans are so dominant," Carleton said. "We have to find ways to hang on to what we have."

Today Carleton is working with other scientists on the U.S. "Man and the Biosphere" program, a concept begun in 1972 as the International Biological Program but which expanded to include the marine environment as well. Involved in the program are the U.S. State Department, the National Oceanographic and Atmospheric Administration (NOAA), the U.S. Forest Service and the National Park Service, among others. The Man and the Biosphere scientists are looking at "the big balance, the big picture."

"We need an Einstein and a half for this," Carleton said. "You have to take into account the geological processes that have taken millions of years to evolve, as well as phytoplankton, which takes seconds. You have to look at the interaction of every living thing, including man. Light a match to hydrogen and you get an explosion every time. With living organisms, you never know. Man is unpredictable."

Because of Carleton, I dropped my special-interest campaigning in 1971. From him I had learned that when something difficult needs to be solved, one should look at the total picture rather than reacting to only one side. Although adventurous people often make their moves before knowing all they need to know, sensationalism is a poor substitute for earnest endeavor. Beneath every lasting work that results in a real solution for mankind is usually a foundation of careful thought.

### Suggested Reading

Carleton Ray and Elgin Ciampi, *The Underwater Guide to Marine Life* (A. S. Barnes and Company: New York, 1956).

## Chapter 13

*Eugenie Clark*

# Eugenie Clark: Shark Lady

*Life was meant to be lived,*
*and curiosity must be kept alive.*
*One must never, for whatever reason,*
*turn his back on life.*

— *Eleanor Roosevelt*

I n 1931 Eugenie Clark, age nine, had been left by her mother at the old aquarium in Battery Park that used to stand at the tip of Manhattan. Her mother was on her way to work and told Eugenie to amuse herself. Eugenie pressed her face against the glass of one of the larger aquariums and tried to see through the pale green mist of the water. She pretended she was walking on the bottom of the sea.

"So casually, so by chance," Eugenie recalled later, "I entered the world of water."[1]

From these beginnings at the Battery Park Aquarium, Eugenie's youthful curiosity expanded into important research on all sorts of fishes—the odd Moses sole of the Red Sea, the sleeping sharks of Mexico, the mysterious "flashlight fish" of the Red Sea, the plectognaths of the South Pacific and other strange and previously unknown marine life.

However, at the top, middle and bottom of Eugenie's list of ichthyological subjects are sharks. She is called "The Shark Lady," and for good reason. She has swum with them, trained them, lived and breathed with them. The book, *The Lady and the Sharks,* published in 1969, details her experiences with these mysterious animals. Considered a world expert on sharks, she writes regularly for *National Geographic* and has been the subject of numerous television specials. If I were to recall my first impressions upon meeting Eugenie, it is that she is open, always eager to learn something new. I have never seen her unwilling to explore new territories—emotional, philosophical or physical.

The last time I saw her, she stopped over in Santa Barbara on her way to China, and we shared a nonserious evening of storytelling and fooling around. She was then approaching 60, but her curiosity and sense of adventure were still completely childlike. Later I took Eugenie to the airport. Her tennis shoes were untied, and they were still untied when she asked the airlines clerk to check her bags straight through to Peking. She was more preoccupied with where she was going than how she was going.

"We've never checked any bag from Santa Barbara to Peking," the airport employee said. "I'm sure we never have."

"There's always a first time," Eugenie said.

That says it all. Whenever she can, Eugenie will grab that first time if ever it comes her way. Each step she took in her career was often the first taken by anyone in that direction. I think of Eugenie alone in the South Pacific being taught to fish with throw nets by the betel-chewing natives, or in the Sinai desert learning to ride camels and speaking Arabic. I ask myself, would I, like she did, do these things just so that I could further my understanding of what I needed to know? Eugenie never stopped to ask herself such questions. Obstacles of any sort were merely the challenges that moved her forward.

When Eugenie was a young girl, the first obstacle to her insatiable curiosity came from her grandmother. Eugenie brought home toads, salamanders, birds, alligators and just about anything she could catch or wrestle down. Because her pursuits were not encouraged, she always seemed to have a lot of dead things hidden in the closet. Her grandmother wondered why she didn't develop an interest in something more useful, like typing.

One confrontation between them occurred when Eugenie wanted to have a look at a rat skeleton. She had a dead rat handy, but it was necessary for her to boil it first. While her grandmother was away from the house one day, she got the rat into a pot of water and turned it on high. Her grandmother returned suddenly, wanting to know what was cooking.

Lack of encouragement seemed to follow her, even in later years. After obtaining a bachelor's degree in zoology from Hunter College in New York, Eugenie applied to Columbia University for her doctorate. She was told in essence, "Go home, get married, and have babies."

When I consider Eugenie meeting this kind of resistance, I am reminded of how young people often know in what direction their life's interest lie. These early interests are the seeds that will bloom into successful life if only the seed is watered by faith and nurtured through perseverance. Too often curiosity and desire are withered by doubt—either from timid guardians or friends without such a sense of adventure. Too often we are led into dull safety, following paths and patterns set by others.

Eugenie didn't wither from the discouragements placed upon her. Instead, she acquired more fish to study. Then in 1942 she was finally admitted to the doctorate program at New York University. After receiving her master's degree, Eugenie went to California to work as a research assistant at Scripps Institute in La Jolla under Dr. Carl L. Hubbs. Hubbs was conducting some innovative studies in the waters off Southern California. Under his guidance, Eugenie was introduced to diving with a hard hat.

Her first obstacle nearly became a disaster. She was diving with the hard-hat equipment when her air hose jammed. She began to pass out before she realized what was happening, but managed to abandon the helmet and return to surface. When she was pulled to the ship by Dr. Hubbs, he insisted that she get back into the water almost immediately. He wouldn't allow her time to develop any fears about diving. With a short rest after her near disaster, Eugenie was back down in the hard-hat gear, walking around with the fishes.

Although free diving, using only mask, fins and snorkel, seems less complicated than hard-hat or scuba diving, it is actually more difficult in many ways. Time and time again the diver must return to the surface for air, then descend again to observe or spear a fish. When Eugenie received a fellowship from the Pacific Science Board in 1948 to study blowfish in the South Seas, free diving was the only method she could use to make her observations. Because compressed air on remote islands was unattainable, Eugenie learned free diving and spearfishing from a Palauan named Siakong. Siakong, she said, was the best diver in the world. He wore only a small red loincloth and homemade goggles when he dived.

He and Eugenie took a small boat to the reefs off Koror. There Siakong taught his pupil how to use a thrownet to catch fish. He also showed her how to use the spears he had made from bamboo and metal. Siakong could catch fish empty-handed. He knew the best places to catch plectognaths (triggerfishes and blowfishes), and had the remarkable capacity to stay down on one breath seemingly forever. He would go down, hang onto a piece of coral and wait for the fish to come to him.

One day Eugenie went down to watch Siakong in action. She reached for a piece of coral to hold herself down. Then the coral moved. What she had grasped was the side of a giant "man-eating" clam.

"The clam had just snapped shut and my fingers were only a fraction of an inch from the opening between the two halves of the shell," Eugenie recalled.[2]

Siakong hadn't yet revealed all of his talents. One day as she was diving with him and another native Niraibui, she spotted Siakong caught in a clam. "The jaws

*During one of many trips to the Red Sea, Dr. Genie Clark encounters the flashlight fish.*

Photo by David Doubilet

of the gigantic mollusk were clamped tight," Eugenie said, "and Siakong's arm was in it up to the elbow. Siakong wasn't moving."[3]

Eugenie came to the surface and started yelling at Niraibui in panic. Just as she was about to dive again, Siakong popped up beside them, grinning. He held up the adductor muscle of the clam with the arm that had been "caught" between the jaws of the mollusk. As they all got into the boat, the men laughed at Eugenie for her undue display of fright. Then they made a meal of the muscle.

Eugenie collected all of her samples using methods she learned from Siakong, and her blowfish studies were a success. Still maintaining a balance between adventuresome research and formal education, she returned to New York University where, in 1950, she received her Doctor of Philosophy degree. Then she won a Fulbright Scholarship to conduct a one-year study of poisonous fishes in the Red Sea.

At the time, the Red Sea was relatively unknown to scientist and traveller alike. Eugenie set out alone, with no idea what she would see. She arrived in Cairo on Christmas Eve, 1950. Two weeks later she was in Ghardaia, at the eastern edge of the Libyan desert, where she saw for the first time the marine biological station that was to be her home for the next year. The station consisted of an office building, library, museum, engine house and two cottages for visiting scientists; but Eugenie noted that there were seldom more than two or three

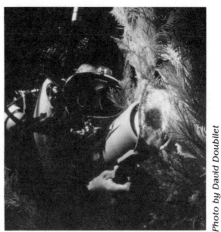

*Photo by David Doubilet*

*Photo by David Doubilet*

*Dr. Clark swims the Red Sea with the Moses Sole (left) and in Japan finds the egg case of a swell shark, (above) with embryo intact.*

scientists at the station at a time. Her cottage bordered the edge of the desert on one side and the Red Sea on the other.

> At high tide I could just reach my quarters and still keep my feet dry. Nearby was a pink-and-white-striped building, the natives' mosque. From my window I saw the worshipers come down to the sea and wash themselves before going in to the mosque to pray. And then I could hear the voice of the muezzin and the chanting of the passages from the Koran.[4]

Eugenie learned to speak the Arabic dialect so that she could communicate with the locals who helped her. The houseboy and cook so pampered her that she could devote all her time to studying fish. Veiled women eventually accepted the American scientist who worked in a bathing suit. Eugenie was almost always in a bathing suit, since she dived as often as she could in order to observe and study the fishes and marine life.

"An ichthyologist in a strange land has everything in his favor," Eugenie said. "There is a natural urge in all people to help a stranger—whether it springs from a sincere desire to help, an impulse to show off or mere curiosity to get one's nose in closer."[5]

Eugenie's studies in the Red Sea marked the beginning of her lifelong love for this part of the world. Since then she has made dozens of trips to the Red Sea to study the sharks, eels and fish. Here, she has made some important discoveries. Until the time of Eugenie's first visit in 1950, the Red Sea had been all but overlooked by scientists. After her studies, however, ichthyologists and marine biologists from all over the world flocked to the area.

From her experiences in the South Pacific and the Red Sea came Eugenie's first book, *Lady with a Spear,* published in 1953. The recounting of her South Pacific fishing adventures with Siakong and the hurdles she overcame to live in the Sinai desert captivated a worldwide reading public. The book has been translated into eight languages and Braille.

Two people enthralled with *Lady with a Spear* were William and Anne Vanderbilt. They approached Eugenie with the idea of setting up a marine laboratory in Western Florida as a center where scientists could work in their studies about the sea. Eugenie eagerly accepted the Vanderbilts' offer, and this marked the beginning of her intense study of sharks.

In January, 1955 Eugenie opened the doors of the Cape Haze Marine Laboratory, founded by William H. and Alfred G. Vanderbilt. The lab itself was a small 12-foot by 20-foot wooden building, and Eugenie had a small dock with an adjacent shark pen. Eugenie spent 12 years at Cape Haze. She caught and studied over 2,000 sharks, getting in the water with them to study their behavior and test their memories and ability to learn. She taught sharks to push a target and ring a bell for "reward" food. She trained them to choose between targets of different designs and colors. She found that sharks can make visual discriminations, choosing one color over another. Most startling, she found that sharks remember what they learn. They can discriminate between light and dark and recognize the difference between horizontal and vertical stripes.

Eugenie's unusual experiments with sharks became known around the world. In the fall of 1965, she visited Japan and was invited to the palace of the Crown Prince. As a gift, Eugenie took along a trained shark which performed its tricks for the Crown Prince and his court. The prince was delighted, his curiosity for the underwater world aroused. He asked Eugenie to teach him to dive, and she did.

In 1967, Eugenie left Cape Haze and moved back to New York. The lab went under the direction of her associate and colleague, Dr. Perry Gilbert, and was eventually renamed Mote Marine Laboratory. Eugenie's shark studies there are the subject of her book, *The Lady and the Sharks,* published in 1969.

By this time, sharks were about to become a world curiosity. In 1969 Peter Gimbel was filming *Blue Water–White Death. Jaws* came later in 1973. There was a lot of shark hysteria and dramatization. Eugenie stayed apart from the drama and continued her research.

142

It has long been thought that sharks, especially the fast-swimming species, have to keep moving in order to breathe, flushing oxygen-rich water over their gills. But in 1972 Eugenie received a letter from Mexican photographer Ramon Bravo. His photographs showed sharks sleeping in a cave off Isla Mujeres. Mexican divers reported seeing four species there—blue, lemon, ridgeback and bull—all dangerous to man, and never known to remain stationary.

Eugenie's curiosity was aroused. If whatever caused the sharks to be so docile could be duplicated, perhaps shark attacks on swimmers could be reduced. She made an excursion to Isla Mujeres during Thanksgiving of that year, but found no sharks. In April 1973, Eugenie returned again, this time with support from the National Geographic Society and the Mexican Consejo National de Turisma. Three of her four children accompanied her as assistants, as did several of her students.

During her first dive into the sleeping shark cave at Isla Mujeres, Eugenie observed that all the sharks were of one species, *Carcharhinus springeri* (a ridgeback of the requiem family). Instead of being agitated by the presence of humans, the sharks remained in the sort of stupor that Bravo had described. However, Eugenie saw that the sharks did not really seem to "sleep," but watched all of the human movements in the cave.

It was very unusual behavior, and Eugenie looked for clues. She and her students found remoras actively cleaning the "sleeping" sharks, and observed that the oxygen level in the deepest, dead-end parts of the cave was higher than normal. Eugenie reasoned that the high levels of oxygen enabled the sharks to lie still for hours. The students postulated that the sharks enjoyed some sort of "high" by exposing themselves to a possible electromagnetic field created by the mingling of fresh and salt waters in the cave. Another student discovered carbon dioxide was present in above-normal amounts, and reasoned that this could have an anesthetic effect on some sharks.

Swimming past these anesthetized animals, Eugenie wondered whether fish sleep the way humans or other animals sleep. She wondered if sharks slept anywhere else in the world. After numerous trips to Mexico to the caves at Isla Mujeres, La Punta, El Puente and La Cadena, Eugenie got her chance to pursue this unanswered question in Japan.

In 1976 she went to Japan with graduate student Anita George and her 75-year-old stepfather, Nobusan. There, the team searched the marine countryside for "shark dormitories". What they found astonished them. In one bay alone, over 100 sharks, some swimming, some thrashing in shallow water and some in caves, were piled on top of each other, sleeping. Eugenie and her assistants stood knee deep in water and recorded the whole scene by bending over, holding the camera underwater while scores of sharks swam by them. In Mexico Eugenie had found only one species of shark in the caves, but in Japan, she found both white-tip reef sharks and the smaller Japanese requiem sharks.

In 1978 she accompanied a filming expedition to the Great Barrier Reef in Australia, where underwater filmmaker Stan Waterman was documenting the great white shark for a television special. Eugenie conducted several experiments, but in particular, she wanted to test the effect of the Moses sole on the great white shark.

During her studies in the Red Sea, Eugenie had discovered that the odd Moses sole (*Pardachirus marmoratus*) has a milky fluid that kills small fishes. She tested the reaction of sharks to the sole itself and found the sharks always avoided this fish. However, if the Moses sole were "washed" with alcohol, a shark would eat it right up. The alcohol obviously removed the sole's poisonous fluid— but what was the fluid? It had been reported by an ichthyologist in 1871, but no one knew it was toxic until Eugenie began her Red Sea experiments. She suspected that the fluid could serve as an effective shark repellent, since in one test she observed that a thimbleful could keep sharks away up to 18 hours. Not long after she discovered this, one company combined the fluid with a suntan lotion.

Eugenie learned that Japan had its own version of this highly toxic sole, and Australia did, too. All toxic soles are called *Pardachirus,* and there are four known species.

Eugenie's research had resulted in a list of honors and awards that is practically endless. She is written about in *Who's Who in the East, Who's Who in America, Who's Who in the World, Who's Who in the South and Southwest,* and *World Who's Who in Science.* She has received awards from the Underwater Society of America, the American Littoral Society and the Gold Medal Award of the Society of Women Geographers. With her "leftover" time, Eugenie has worked to preserve the unique environment of the Red Sea. She was collaborating on a conservation program for the area with Egyptian leader Anwar Sadat at the time of his assassination. After his death, she continued to push for the establishment of a marine park off Ras Muhammad, at the very tip of the Sinai. She volunteered her aid to the Holy Land Conservation Fund, which worked to preserve the environment of the Red Sea, and she volunteered to serve as a ranger in the Sinai Marine Reserve. The underwater reefs around the Sinai and Ras Muhammad, she said, make up "one of the most spectacular underwater areas in the world."

Eugenie encourages young people to get involved in what interests them most. Today, she nearly always takes a number of her students with her on her research trips, which are heavily scheduled throughout the year and involve the use of deep-sea submersibles. When I last heard from Eugenie, she was diving to 2,000 feet in the Caribbean to study deep-sea sharks, tripod fish, deep-water

Photo by David Doubilet

Dr. Genie Clark

moray eels, snake mackerels and "other fish never seen alive before."[6] The printed schedule she sent me was typed on May 4, her birthday. She pointed out that she had just hit the "big 65".

Her own goals haven't changed much from when she was nine. She still wants to understand everything about fish. Because of that enduring goal, Eugenie has advanced scientific vision and enlarged the concept of underwater adventure. What began "so casually, so by chance" has become an inspiration to diving men and women all over the world.

### Notes

1. Eugenie Clark, *Lady With a Spear* (Harper & Brothers Publishers: New York, 1953) p. 109.
2. *Ibid.*
3. *Ibid.*
4. *Ibid.,* p. 178.
5. *Ibid.,* p. 180.
6. Personal communication from Eugenie Clark to Hillary Hauser.

### Suggested Reading

Eugenie Clark, *Lady with a Spear* (Harper & Brothers Publishers: New York, 1951).
Eugenie Clark, *The Lady and the Sharks* (Harper & Row: New York, 1969).
Eugenie Clark, "Into the Lairs of 'Sleeping' Sharks" (*National Geographic Magazine,* April 1975).

## Chapter 14

*Dr. Sylvia Earle*

# Sylvia Earle:
# Her Deepness

*We cannot discover new oceans*
*unless we have the courage*
*to lose sight of the shore.*

— *Andre Gide*

I felt like a hawk as I left the submarine and swam out freely along the face of this submerged cliff, knowing that more than 3,000 feet below was just empty, blue, deep, open water. It was like swimming into the sky on the side of a mountain. I wanted to spread my arms and take off.[1]

That is how Sylvia Earle, aquanaut, oceanographer and ichthyo-botanist, remembers swimming at 250 feet in the Tongue of the Ocean, an area of great depth off the Bahamas. It was April 1975, and she was participating in SCORE (Scientific Cooperative Operational Research Expedition), a major undersea operation in the Caribbean. For the first time, major undersea firms had joined together to study underwater reef environments. The divers, including Sylvia, stayed one week in *Hydro-Lab*, an undersea habitat at 60 feet, and were shuttled in the submersible *Johnson-Sea-Link* to the face of a vertical coral wall at 250 feet. Here, in water that dropped off to 3,000 feet, the divers locked out of the sub for 45 minutes and swam along the wall to look at the reef environment. Sylvia swam and explored for two days in a row this way, only to learn later that she had made the longest and deepest lockout dives ever performed by a woman.

Sylvia is not new to saturation diving. She has spent thousands of hours saturated in various subsea habitats and even more hours free diving, scuba diving and working with hard-hat and hookah gear. She has locked out of submarines, dived in strange and exotic seas all over the globe, and discovered many new species of marine algae. Because of her numerous experiences in living underwater for extended periods of time, Sylvia is known as one of the leading aquanauts of the world. She is affectionately called "Her Deepness".

I had heard of Sylvia for several years before I finally got to talk with her in 1976. I was writing the book, *Women in Sports: Scuba Diving* and wanted to include her in one of the chapters because I knew she had dared to be different.

For the interview, Sylvia came to my house, and immediately we began to talk about things other than her career. We talked about life, love and the pursuit of happiness. We talked about what we felt and what we wanted to do. Then the day was over. We passed an entire afternoon in this wonderful dialogue, and at the end of it, realized we had accomplished nothing of what we had intended to do. I think this is common for an adventurer like Sylvia. She is more interested in the present action and in moving forward than in looking behind and contemplating past accomplishments.

"I'll tell you what," Sylvia said. "Let's go to my house, which isn't far from here, and I'll just give you everything that's been written about me and you can use that."

The stack of books and magazines she handed me contained big stories and minor snippets about her accomplishments. There were also serious scientific papers about species of algae she had discovered and named.

I asked Sylvia how she got into the ocean business, and she said it was because she's "always enjoyed taking a bath." Born in Gibbstown, New Jersey, in August 1935, she spent many vacations at Ocean City. There, she fell in love with the sea. She fished for eels and crabs and spent many hours alone in the woods, thinking, running, collecting flowers. Her parents, though they are not involved in such pursuits themselves, never discouraged her.

"I was turned loose with a watchful eye, but without the 'Great No' which dulls the curiosity of so many children," Sylvia said. "The 'Great No'—that's the 'don't pick up frogs, don't go into the water, don't do this, don't do that.' My parents encouraged my curiosity. My inclinations are a reflection of theirs in that they are open and responsive people."

When Sylvia was twelve, her family moved to Florida near the Gulf of Mexico, where she became acquainted with sea urchins and starfish. She spent a lot of time in the water splashing around in an unsophisticated way. In 1953 when she was a sophomore at Florida State University, she took a course in biology. Her professor, Dr. Harold Humm, became a great influence in her life both at Florida State and, later, at Duke University.

That summer Sylvia spent eight weeks totally engrossed in studying ocean plants and animals with seven other students in a field station in northern Florida. That was her first introduction to scuba diving. She was given a chance to try one of the two-hose units available to the class. Her instruction consisted of the simple advice not to hold her breath.

"I took about three breaths and I was breathing naturally," she recalled. "It was, 'Gasp, gasp. Oh! I'm a fish!' There was something to do and something to see—fishes in a turtlegrass bed and lots of action. They almost had to haul me back to get me out of the water."

Her first attention was devoted to crabs, for which Sylvia says she had a passion. She entertained herself that summer learning all about them. In subsequent studies, she became increasingly interested in the basis of all life: photosynthesis. Her attention eventually focused on marine algae, where it has stayed ever since. "They are the producers," Sylvia said. She likes to tease her zoologist colleagues by reminding them that without plants, even *they* would not exist.

"Everything on this earth is dependent upon plants, whether above water or below," Sylvia said. "Everything on the table, on the fishes' menu—everything is from the energy of the sun, which is locked into the food source through photosynthesis."

Sylvia received her Ph.D. from Duke University. Today she is one of the world's first diving botanists. As she goes deep into the sea to conduct first-hand studies, she finds that she is also the first in a lot of other areas. "I'm not doing it for that reason," she said. "I'm driven by a compelling curiosity."

Sylvia's curiosity has kept her going beyond reasonable hours in a library, at her desk or over a microscope, pressing farther and deeper into the ocean depths. Her curiosity has netted her a long list of achievements, all made at the same time she was managing a household of children. Elizabeth, Richie and Gale often go along with their mother as surface assistants.

Between 1966 and 1967, Sylvia directed the Cape Haze Marine Lab, established by Eugenie Clark in 1955. She has held research appointments at the Farlow Herbarium at Harvard, the University of Southern Florida Marine Science Institute at St. Petersburg and the Los Angeles County Museum of Natural History, and she received an appointment from the California Academy of Sciences at Berkeley.

Sylvia does not believe it is necessary for young people to wait until they are so-called "adults" before they take major steps in pursuing their interests. In her late teens she started collecting and cataloguing every known species of algae along the 1,000-mile eastern coastline of the Gulf of Mexico. She had her

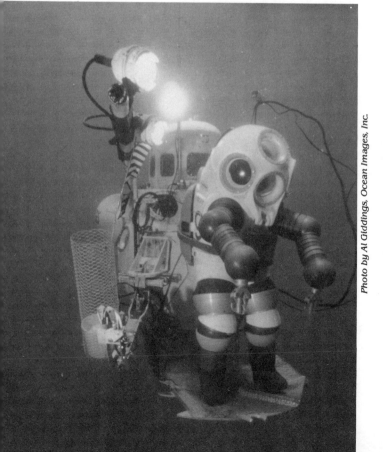

*Dr. Alice Alldredge surfaces in WASP (top), while Dr. Sylvia Earle explores the underwater world (above and left) with the aid of a pressurized diving suit.*

bachelor's degree at 19, her master's degree at 20. She has made some important discoveries.

She has found and named several new species and genera of algae. During the SCORE project, she discovered a new genus of plant at 250 feet, which she named *Johnson Sea Linkia* after the submersible that took her there. The plant was later seen growing in 500-foot depths. One genus of red algae she named after Harold Humm.

"The plant in question is a small plant about four inches high, with many soft, fingerlike branches that extend above it," she explained. "It looked like a little umbrella, so I named it *Hummbrella!*" Her tongue-in-cheekiness was frowned upon by some of her colleagues, but Sylvia said, "How could I resist?"

As Sylvia pushed deeper and deeper into the sea, she discovered that photosynthesis can occur where light intensity is far less than anyone previously thought was required. What makes it possible, she found, is that the accessory pigments of algae, which the more highly evolved green plants on land do not have, enable the algae to absorb light that is then converted to chlorophyll. Before her direct deep-water observations, she, like other scientists, believed that the maximum depth at which plants could grow was roughly 300 feet.

As a scientist, Sylvia's main interest is in the depth ranges marine plants can grow. Diving, she feels, is the "vehicle" that gets her there. The fact that she is thought of as an aquanaut amuses her somewhat. "The inaccessibility, the concern that many people have about subjecting themselves to the circum-stances to see what goes on . . . that largely is the reason these things aren't studied," she said. "They're not studied enough—we're just beginning to know."

Sylvia lives in habitats and travels in submersibles so that she can stay underwater for days among the fishes and plants. In 1968 she went with inventor Ed Link (designer of the *Johnson-Sea-Link*) on an expedition involving the use of the submersible *Deep Diver*. She locked out at various depths to study deep-water plants in places along the vertical drop-offs in the Tongue of the Ocean. She stayed out of the sub for one-and-a-half hours and decompressed in the sub on the way back to the surface. In doing so, Sylvia was the first woman to take part in Link's Man-in-Sea program, in which the *Deep Diver* played a significant role.

In the summer of 1969, *Tektite I* was launched in 50 feet of water in Lameshur Bay in the Virgin Islands. In this submerged four-room habitat, four scientist–aquanauts lived underwater for a record-breaking two months. That same year plans for *Tektite II* began to be formulated, and scientists were asked to submit proposals to indicate what each of them could do with two weeks underwater. Sylvia submitted an application.

Later she learned that her application had created a stir in the U.S. Department of Interior. Department officials were not prepared for women applicants. Others besides Sylvia had applied. "What do we do with these women?" they asked. Sylvia had suggested that she go with some ichthyologist colleagues of hers because she wanted to study food chains. It would be profitable, she thought, to go down with people who really knew fishes. She had given no thought to the question of who was male and who was female. She discovered that the idea was frowned upon by the Washington people, who questioned the advisability of putting women and men together for a couple of weeks underwater.

Out of this came an all-woman team of aquanauts with Sylvia as their leader. This was the first time scientists had been involved as aquanauts on a nationwide underwater project. That this would also be the first time women worked as aquanauts was of secondary importance.

Sylvia's team consisted of Dr. Ann Hurley, an animal ecologist at Scripps Institution in La Jolla; Dr. Renate True, then a biological oceanographer at Tulane; and Alina Szmant, an animal ecologist at Scripps. Their engineer, Peggy Lucas, had limited diving experience, but, as Sylvia put it, "She had a cool head— the most important characteristic of being a good diver." Peggy had the job of pushing buttons and maintaining the habitat. Only Ann and Alina knew one another before meeting for the project.

"All the other teams were selected because they had mutual interests," Sylvia reflected. "We were brought together because those in Washington seemed to think it was 'safer' to keep the women together."

The five women became fast friends as a result of their 14 days together underwater and the six weeks total that it took to complete the entire project. In part, their close tie was because of political pressure from above, but also due to their unique and mutually appreciated opportunity to stay with the fishes.

"One of the best things," Sylvia said, "was that we ceased to be visitors and became residents. We had *our* cave and the fishes had theirs. We got out and worked day and night, and they did the same. You're one of them. You don't say, 'those angelfishes, these damselfishes, those barracudas,' but, 'that barracuda, this angelfish, that filefish that lives under that rock.' You get to know them as individuals, as neighbors."

After 21 hours of decompression, the women emerged to an enthusiastic public. They had shown that there were no handicaps in being women. A team of psychologists determined that they not only held their own, but exceeded the other teams on some fronts. ("Those were by *their* yardsticks, not ours," Sylvia said.) The women had spent more time in the water, were well-organized, were good housekeepers, and had no squabbles. They had been watched and monitored for 24 hours a day by closed-circuit television. They came out "right at the top."

*Exploring the ocean in Deep
Rover is an event above,
as well as below the surface.*

Sylvia was quick to state that all of the women contributed to their success, but because she was the team leader, much of the attention focused on her. They received the Conservation Service Award from the Department of Interior, the highest recognition the Department gives to civilians. In receiving the award, Sylvia accepted on behalf of her team and for all of the *Tektite* aquanauts, commenting, "We went primarily as scientists and engineers, incidentally as women and men."

"Now, years later," Sylvia said, "I've stopped apologizing for being a woman. There is no reason to apologize or feel anything but a feeling of pride. I am a woman and that is good. There are things I can accomplish as a woman and as a scientist, as both."

The team was whisked around the country, first to Washington, then Chicago, New York and Los Angeles, to talk and be interviewed. In Chicago, Sylvia was named an honorary citizen; in Washington, she was feted at the White House; and in Los Angeles, she became the *Times* Woman of the Year.

These recognitions and accolades never encouraged Sylvia to rest on her laurels. Afterward, she doubled her research efforts. In 1972 she went to the Galapagos and Cocos Islands to collect marine plants. Later that year, she participated in another saturation diving project in the Florida Keys. The following year, she participated in a study-observation visit to the People's Republic of China, where she travelled as one of 14 professional colleagues in six cities of that country. In 1975 she went to the Comoro Islands as part of a California Academy of Sciences expedition to capture a live coelacanth. A coelacanth (pronounced SEAL-a-canth) is a prehistoric fish once thought to be extinct until one was caught in the net of a fisherman. Scientists have worked hard to capture and keep one alive in captivity.

Sylvia said she was looking to the day where women and men could work side by side with no thought for gender. Perhaps in part because of the success of Sylvia's team during the *Tektite* project, little thought is now given to men and women working together underwater. During several saturation dives in *Hydrolab* from 1973 to 1975, Sylvia led teams of two men and two women, one man and three women, and, twice, three men and one woman.

Sylvia remembered the commotion following the *Tektite* dive.

"The whole point seemed to be that we were female," Sylvia said. "If we were good, that should have been enough. In time, that *will* be enough. Perhaps for now it is good that people are noticing."

Since those early days as an aquanaut, Sylvia has expanded her underwater explorations into the world of one-man submersibles that allow her to dive deep for longer periods of time. In 1979 Sylvia made a world record solo untethered dive to 1,250 feet off Oahu, Hawaii. Her vehicle was the JIM, a one-man submersible shaped like a moon suit, which allows a diver to stay in deep water while remaining at surface atmospheric pressure. It eliminates the need for lengthy decompression at the end of the dive to avoid the dreaded "bends".

Soon after, she was trained to dive in other one-man submersibles, including *Mantis,* a diving machine that resembles the insect for which it was named. *Mantis* was developed by Graham Hawkes, a British engineer who has designed more than 20 submersible systems, including *Wasp, Mantis, Deep Rover,* and the remotely operated systems *Bandit* and *Phantom.* The manipulators he engineered for his submersibles have also been used in outer space, for work requiring delicacy and precision.

Sylvia and Graham now apply their mutual knowledge and experience to their business, Deep Ocean Technology, to provide submersible systems to the offshore oil industry, as well as to provide equipment for scientific ocean research.

Her Deepness is quick to remind us that the average depth of the Pacific is 13,739 feet, and the average depth of the Atlantic is 12,257 feet. These figures represent a lot of unexplored territory on this planet. With advanced submersibles, man may eventually see much of it. There is more down there than oil, gold and shipwrecks. The quest of deep-diving man is knowledge, and the exploration of the very deep seafloor will eventually unlock the secrets of undersea galaxies all over the world.

## Notes

1. Hillary Hauser, *Women in Sports: Scuba Diving* (Harvey House, Publishers: New York, 1976), p. 59.

## Suggested Reading

Hillary Hauser, *Women in Sports: Scuba Diving* (Harvey House, Publishers: New York, 1976).

Sylvia A. Earle and Al Giddings, *Exploring the Deep Frontier* (National Geographic Society: Washington, D.C., 1980).

John G. Vanderwalker, "Science's Window on the Sea" and Sylvia A. Earle, "All-Girl Team Tests the Habitat" (*National Geographic Magazine,* August 1971).

## Chapter 15

*John Lilly*

# John Lilly:
# Searching the Unsearchable

*Imagination,
not invention,
is the supreme master
of art as of life.*

— *Joseph Conrad*

———

Within the next decade or two the human species will establish communication with another species: nonhuman, alien, possibly extraterrestrial, more probably marine; but definitely highly intelligent, perhaps even intellectual. An optimistic prediction, I admit.[1]

So John C. Lilly predicted in 1960 in his preface to *Man and Dolphin*. The book outlines his revolutionary experiments in talking with dolphins at his Communication Research Institute in St. Thomas, U.S. Virgin Islands.

In 1959 Dr. Lilly and his scientific team created an underwater environment complete with hydrophones and underwater loudspeakers so that man and dolphin could speak to each other. This was not the work of a Frankenstein gone mad, but the outgrowth of Lilly's many years of serious medical research on the human brain. A graduate of Caltech and the University of Pennsylvania Medical School, Lilly was, by 1949, involved in the probing of the human mind. He had studied at the National Institute of Mental Health as a United States Public Health Service Officer. (The institute later provided him with a five-year Career Award providing financial support for his dolphin research in St. Thomas.) Lilly's revolutionary concept of interspecies communication inspired the popular movie, *Day of the Dolphin*, based on his research experiences at the Virgin Islands laboratory.

This project is not the only unusual product of Lilly's unique mind. In 1954 he began a series of experiments on human isolation from all senses—sight, sound, hearing and feeling. He created the "isolation tank", in which a person could float in the darkness and silence of a closed capsule filled with body temperature water. With no light to see or sounds to hear, with body and water temperature equal, a person could "be nowhere else but in his own mind," Lilly said. This work, outlined in his books, *Programming and Metaprogramming in the Human Biocomputer* and *The Center of the Cyclone,* inspired the motion picture, *Altered States.*

Lilly's controversial experiments have been frowned upon by more serious scientists, who believe that scientific research should remain far apart from flightsof the imagination. However, Lilly's unusual projects have inspired two major movies, and this may be an indication of how the public loves to dream. Lilly is right on the edge between the sane and ridiculous, but perhaps this is an edge every innovative thinker has tiptoed upon. Those who go out on a limb, like Columbus, tend to discover new worlds. Even if Lilly is not considered a "scientist" in the pure sense of the word, he is an imaginative explorer. The complicated labyrinths of a researcher's own imagination can provide plenty of adventure.

In 1984 I was assigned to interview Lilly for the *Santa Barbara News–Press.* I was curious to meet the man who had written the many books I'd read following the *Maravilla* expedition in 1972. That summer, as we searched the Little Bahama Bank for the Spanish galleon that had sunk in 1656, we occasionally stopped to swim with the playful dolphins. To write a story about my experiences, I ran into Lilly's work.

At the National Institute of Mental Health, Lilly had discovered a number of dolphin traits that indicated their high intelligence, including their love of play and need of sleep ("cat naps" at the surface). Lilly also noticed the dolphins' uncanny instinct about protecting each other, pointing out that a sick dolphin must be attended 24 hours a day and that one dolphin will perform this duty for another until the sick one recovers. The recovery period can range from several days to weeks, and the faithful dolphin stands by the whole time.

Dolphins and porpoises comprise the family Delphinidae. There are minor physiological differences between the two: the dolphin has a long, snoutlike beak and sharp teeth; the porpoise has spade-shaped teeth and no beak. The physiological differences are minor. Most people, and some scientists, refer to them both as porpoises.

Dolphins and porpoises belong to the scientific order *Cetacea,* which includes the whales. Cetaceans are not fish, but warm-blooded mammals that bear their young alive and nurse them after they are born. While they live completely independent of land, unlike seals and sea lions, they need air to live. A dolphin needs to breathe, on the average, every thirty seconds.

Cetaceans are sometimes called "reentrants" because millions of years ago, they once lived on land. Scientists point to their terrestrial body plan; an X-ray of the flipper of the dolphin would show the bone of a hand, forearm, wrist, fingers

*Dolphins are intelligent, as well as very social creatures.*

and upper arm. The nose has moved to the top of the head to form the blowhole. With this, the dolphin can breathe without lifting its head from the water.

The dolphin has a sonar so highly developed that it outclasses anything created by our highest technologies. The best of sonars available to humans, in use by the U.S. Navy, can only indicate an object in the distance. Whether it is a whale or a submarine often cannot be distinguished. The dolphin, on the other hand, can discern not only whether the thing is a whale or submarine, but it can tell what kind of metal it is (if it's a submarine), or whether it is dead or alive (if it's a whale). The sonar of the dolphin tells the animal the size, direction, distance, shape, density, movement and texture of the object in question.

There is a peculiar awareness within porpoises of the intelligence of man, which is one purported reason that porpoises adapt so readily in captivity. Dolphins have been known to exhibit excessive faithfulness toward their trainers, sometimes returning to them even when set free in the open ocean.

The Greeks called dolphins *Hieros ichthys,* the "sacred fish." Throughout time dolphins have been respected, admired and worshiped as intelligent brothers of the sea. Troubled mariners on rough waters always regarded their appearance as a good sign—an indication of safety. The animals have often been

159

fantasized or idealized to have extraterrestrial connections—so intelligent, some say, that they speak a language we puny humans cannot duplicate or decipher. This is where Lilly considered the matter, for his background was heavily steeped in mind work.

Lilly is intense, as one might expect a mind-researcher to be. During our interview, he spent more time thinking than talking. He and his wife, Antoinetta (Toni), were, at the time, building a spa in the sunny Mexican coastal town of Costa Careyes, near Puerto Vallarta, Mexico. There, humans and dolphins could come together and interact in a shallow bay. The Lillys described their Mexican project as a place where people would be able to swim, snorkel or sit on the beach, regenerating soul and body and communicating with dolphins.

"You get a perspective on awareness that you can't get from just talking to other humans," Toni Lilly said. "You begin to understand your own humanness."

The idea behind the dolphin spa (which they had tentatively called Delphi) was not only to create a place where people could come and "detoxify", but also to get dolphins and humans together. The most important thing, she said, was to get dolphins and children together. Children can more easily communicate and pick up new languages, whereas adults are programmed, Toni Lilly said.

"Have you seen *E.T.?*" she asked me. "That is exactly the kind of thing we are talking about."

The idea of the Costa Careyes project was that dolphins could swim into the cove freely, mingle with the humans and even participate in underwater birthing. Dolphins could participate in the birthing process, Lilly said, a procedure not unusual for a highly intelligent animal known to help mankind in trouble at sea. He felt that the best time for interspecies communication between man and dolphin was at the moment of birth, or at least when a child is very young. After that, the limitations of adulthood enter in.

Lilly, whose work has resulted in dozens of scientific papers and books (his books include *Man and Dolphin, The Dolphin in History,* and *The Mind of the Dolphin*), said he believes that when man communicates successfully with these mammals, he learns something about his own origins.

Working with Elvar the dolphin, Lilly reported that within several weeks after the dolphin first heard human voices, the animal's vocalization became "less delphinese and to break up into more humanoid, wordlike, explosive bursts of Donald Duckish quacking."

Through all of the experiments Lilly maintained that the important thing was not so much that dolphins should speak like humans—but that humans should accept the idea that highly intelligent species may be able to communicate through a language far more sophisticated than words.

In the movie, *Day of the Dolphin*, the animals actually said things like "Mama" and "Papa". I asked Lilly if this was at all realistic. The movie, he said, was not indicative of how dolphins behave and, in fact, "downgraded" them.

Dolphin communication, he said, is more on the level of telepathy, an expression of inner feelings. "The talk is more of an appeal to pain or happiness, more body language," said Lilly. "It's psychic."

I asked Lilly what he considered the most exciting day of his scientific work.

"It was the day when I realized Elvar was a human," he said. "It was a sudden intuitional flash, a feeling of weirdness. There was a being on the other side of the (Jenus) screen. He was reacting toward us as hard as we reached toward him."

Toni Lilly said people are ready to accept "more spiritual concepts." She also said that science can follow the lead of philosophy. The dolphin spa project in Mexico would have a significant impact on science, she said. Where science is often predetermined by the design of the experiment, in the Costa Careyes experiment the design would not predetermine the results because of its "free-flow nature".

"My husband is not a normal scientist," she said.

Lilly said the isolation tank he invented is a way of "getting inside oneself" and that he still used it to relax. He added that he does nothing systematically—"in food, sleep, you name it."

At the time of our interview, he was working on another book, *From Here to Allternity*. "It's a manual on how to amuse God," Lilly said. "The theme? In any given instant, you have all possibilities open to you—including communications with dolphins. You must keep these possibilities open."

Endless possibility and imagination are the themes of all Lilly's ideas, which can unite artistic thinking with science. Art, he said, is one way of communicating—the sort of inner talk dolphins engage in.

"Art is always in the forefront of science," Lilly said. "Art is the vision of things to come."

### Notes

1. John Lilly, *Man & Dolphin* (Doubleday & Co., Inc.: New York, 1972), p. 19.

### Suggested Reading

John Lilly, *Man & Dolphin* (Doubleday & Co., Inc.: New York, 1961).
John Lilly, *Programming & Metaprogramming in the Human Biocomputer* (Julian Press, Inc.: Crown Publishers, New York, 1972).
John Lilly, *Center of the Cyclone* (Julian Press, Inc., Crown Publishers: New York, 1972).
John Lilly, *The Dolphin in History* (University of California Press: Berkeley, 1963).
John Lilly, *The Mind of the Dolphin: A Non-human Intelligence* (Doubleday: New York, 1967).

## Chapter 16

*Dr. Robert Ballard*

# Robert Ballard:
# Finding the *Titanic*

*And now the matchless deed's achiev'd,*
*Determin'd, dar'd and done.*


— *Christopher Smart*

A t a lobster feed in Gloucester, Massachusetts, in 1972, Robert Ballard leaned over to me and said: "I'm going to find the *Titanic*. Don't tell anyone."

Thirteen years later, in September 1985, Ballard found the *Titanic*. It was a mammoth find—the king of shipwrecks, impossible to locate and impossible to explore since it had been lost in frigid waters over two miles deep. Ballard's find electrified the world. It was like Sir Edmund Hillary's conquest of Mount Everest, or Neil Armstrong's first step onto the moon.

When I heard that Ballard was coming to Santa Barbara, I leaped at the chance to interview him for the *News–Press*. He was appearing at the University of California's campus to accept a Distinguished Alumni Award for his work in the field of oceanography.

As I walked into the campus center, Ballard saw me and roared out a happy greeting. He was going to break away from this publicity madness soon, he said. Would I come along for some fun?

I looked at the other reporters and realized I was simply another media person he would eventually try to escape, but since I was committed to writing the story, I told Ballard why I was there.

When we had talked 13 years earlier in Gloucester, Ballard was working at Woods Hole Oceanographic Institution in Massachusetts. At that time, he conducted deep-ocean dives in submersibles, for the purpose of observing underwater geologic phenomena. His submersible, the *Alvin,* was refitted with a new titanium hull which would extend its diving capacity from 6,000 feet to a depth of 10,000 feet.

This new capability enabled Ballard to explore the Mid-Atlantic Ridge, a deep-sea range of volcanic mountains that divides the Atlantic Ocean roughly in half. The Ridge is part of an undersea mountain chain that encircles the earth. During the early 1970s, the scientific community had begun to form new theories about plate tectonics and the spreading of the sea floor. These scientists wondered if similar functions caused by volcanic activity weren't occurring along the Mid-Atlantic Ridge.

Ballard was convinced that the use of deep-sea submersibles might provide a wealth of information about the deepest, most remote parts of the ocean. However, convincing other people of his idea became a formidable task. He was once derided and nearly laughed out of a meeting of marine geophysicists at Princeton University, where he'd tried to discuss his idea. The scientists had gathered to talk about the geological processes they suspected were occurring along the Mid-Atlantic Ridge, although none of them could offer concrete information.

Ballard suggested the use of deep-sea submersibles to make first-hand observations of the area. The marine specialists told him that no significant science had ever resulted from the use of a submersible.

Ballard was not the sort of person to take "No" for an answer. Undaunted by their negative response, he managed to get one chance to prove his theory. He joined a team of French researchers who shared his eagerness to explore the Mid-Atlantic Ridge with deep-diving submersibles. The French brought in the submersibles *Archimedes* and *Cyana*. Ballard had the *Alvin,* and project FAMOUS (French–American Mid-Ocean Undersea Study) was formed.

The scientists observed and photographed the tectonic plate activity along the ridge, recording molten volcanic rock as it bubbled up from the sea floor and moved away from the ridge on each side. Their observations settled doubts and disputes about the tectonic plate and continental shift activity of Earth.

Following that expedition, Ballard made similar discoveries along the Galapagos Rift, and in the Cayman Trough. He also joined scientists in a series of explorations of deep-sea thermal vents—volcanic cracks in the bottom of the sea where hot gases escape into the surrounding sea water. The scientists discovered that the gases supported strange colonies of sea life where no life was thought possible. The unparalleled successes of these and other deep-diving explorations enabled Ballard to establish and supervise the Deep Submergence Laboratory at Woods Hole.

With *Alvin* capable of diving to 10,000 feet, Ballard could realize his search for the *Titanic.*

*DSV ALVIN being launched from R/V ATLANTIS II each morning.*

Courtesy of Woods Hole Oceanographic Institution

*For the first time in nearly 75 years, eyes — those of a remotely operated camera — look outward from the Titanic, seeing a piece of the ship's ribbing, a railing, and a porthole. The brass rim of the porthole has been kept polished by swift currents, moving along the ocean floor nearly 13,000 feet below the surface of the North Atlantic Ocean. But the ship's ornate woodworking was destroyed, a lavish feast for wood-boring organisms.*

"I thought we could just stretch it a bit, to 13,000 feet," Ballard said.

His idea was not so much to find the Everest of shipwrecks, but to prove that scientists could reach the average depth of the ocean—two miles.

During its maiden voyage in 1912, the "unsinkable" *Titanic* struck an iceberg in the North Atlantic, about 560 miles off Newfoundland. It sank to a depth of 13,120 feet; and 1,522 people died in the disaster. The temperature of the North Atlantic sea was a frigid 28°F, and those of the 2,227 passengers who abandoned ship did not survive for long. The rescue ship *Carpathia* was more than two hours away when it received the *Titanic*'s distress signal.

Ballard wanted to explore the *Titanic*—not to salvage it, but to document it. The advent of the use of undersea robotics gave Ballard the photographic and exploratory tool he needed. Robot-diving vehicles are essentially deep-swimming cameras that explore the depths while those who operated them remain on the surface. The images seen by the submerged camera lenses are relayed to television screens installed on a surface ship, or in a nearby submersible.

With a wide-swath, side-scan sonar system, developed by the French Institute for Research and Exploitation of the Sea, undersea researchers could scan a mile-wide path in the deep ocean. Using this system, Ballard and his French–American team found the *Titanic* on September 1, 1985.

The ship lay on the bottom and was perfectly preserved. "It was whole, up-right, suspended, and very eerie," Ballard said. "We had done so much research

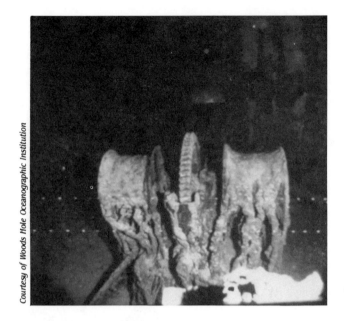

*Courtesy of Woods Hole Oceanographic Institution*

*Electric winch on boat deck near officers' cabin, taken by Jason Jr.*

on the wreck that we were very familiar with the disaster surrounding it. We would swing from elation to depression in moments."

Ballard first descended to the *Titanic* aboard the *Alvin*, along with pilots Ralph Hollis and Dudley Foster. The dive nearly had to be abandoned when the submersible's sonar quit working. However, a navigator aboard the surface ship *Atlantis II* guided the trio to the historic *Titanic* for a first, quick view of the ghostly wreck.

Returning to the massive sunken liner 11 more times, the divers used the "swimming eyeball," a deep-diving, camera-toting robot dubbed *Jason Jr.* With this the explorers produced a series of pictures so graphic and chilling, one can almost mentally relive what happened on the horrible night of April 14, 1912, when the "unsinkable" *Titanic* went down. Published in the December 1985 and December 1986 issues of *National Geographic,* the photos show a bent anchor crane, skewered metal, rusted cables, champagne bottles, a doll's head, silver serving bowls, a set of wooden stairs, a spittoon, a bathtub and many other reminders of how strength and elegance can be so easily reduced to eerie ruins by the sea. In one photograph a sea pen grows on a brass and crystal light. In another the footboard of a bed rests on the sandy mud bottom. The bow of the *Titanic* had been driven deep into the muddy ocean bottom by the enormous momentum of the ship's sinking.

During our interview, Ballard expressed his widely publicized belief that the ship should be made into a memorial. The idea of raising the *Titanic,* he said, is

*An officer's cabin window on the starboard side of the Titanic's boat deck appeared as the manned submersible Alvin surveyed the wreckage of the doomed ship. Alvin, a three-person research vehicle operated by Woods Hole Oceanographic Institution, made eleven dives to the wreckage of the supposedly unsinkable liner, giving the world its first close-up look at the ship since it struck an iceberg on its maiden voyage in 1912 (right).*

*A copper kettle from Titanic's galley lies in the debris field, a third of a mile south of the bow of the great luxury liner at the bottom of the Atlantic Ocean. Strong bottom currents and particles in the water have polished the kettle so that it appears as clean as it was when the ship sank during its maiden voyage on April 15, 1912, bringing death to 1,522 passengers and crewmen. Thousands of artifacts from the Titanic litter the ocean floor (below).*

"ridiculous—a waste of time and money." He also opposes salvaging anything from the *Titanic,* an idea proposed from time to time. An exception, he said, might be to bring up the valuable, "delicate" artifacts scattered around the wreck, which could be housed in a museum. It is estimated that a fortune in jewelry, artworks and other valuables went down with the ship.

Ballard said he supports the Titanic Memorial Act of 1985, a measure that declares the sunken ship an "international maritime memorial" and directs the National Oceanic and Atmospheric Administration (NOAA) to establish guidelines "for conducting research, exploration and, if appropriate, salvage."

The act also ordered the U.S. State Department to fashion an international agreement committing other nations to abide by NOAA rules. The *Titanic,* Ballard explained, lies in international waters. He was optimistic the measure would pass the U.S. Senate, because "anyone who wouldn't want it to pass would be like the Grinch who stole Christmas."

Ballard's immediate plans were to "rest and go to sea" and, otherwise, get on with scientific life. He was tired of the publicity, the fanfare and reporters who hounded him and his family for weeks on end.

Other than the book he was writing about the expedition, *Finding the Titanic,* Ballard said his upcoming plans were to get back to work. Two months after locating the *Titanic,* he was already planning his next expedition, a two-week exploration of deep subsea volcanoes in the Pacific. Using the same deep-sea robotic system he used to locate the historic shipwreck, Ballard's team was going to have a look at the volcanoes residing at 10,000 feet below sea level, on the ocean floor off Mexico. The *Titanic* expedition was "only a test" for the volcano work.

The volcanoes, he said, are in a "ring of fire" that includes the Nevado del Ruiz volcano that had recently erupted in Colombia and buried nearby Armero.

"It will be completely scientific, and you can bet we won't be followed by the media," he said.

Was he planning to go back to the *Titanic?*

"I'm supporting the legislation to leave it alone," Ballard said. "So, I'll abide by the rules."

Not everyone agreed with Ballard's dream of a *Titanic* memorial. In July, 1987, a team of French salvagers pulled their research ship *Nadir* over the spot where the great *Titanic* sank. The same group that had worked with Ballard to locate the ship, now, ironically, returned to salvage it.

For 54 days the British-registered organization (called the Ocean Research Exploration Ltd., but headed by the French Institute for Research and Exploitation of the Sea) planned to conduct a $2.25 million rescue of objects from the sunken liner. The group, headed by Swiss millionaire Carlos Piaget and including a

Hollywood film company, planned to bring up "treasure", including a three-ton strongbox said to hold a fortune in jewels.

In delivering the news of the salvage attempt to the news media, the French institute announced that any material recovered from the *Titanic* would be placed in a public museum and would not be sold. The French spokesmen said the exhibition would "prove as popular as the world tour of the Tutankhamen exhibit."

Using the deep-diving submarine *Nautile* and its robot, *Robin,* the salvagers planned to retrieve any article that "might be worth a fortune."

The French Institute for Research and Exploitation of the Sea ignored Ballard's deep conviction that the ship should remain as a memorial for those who died in the tragedy. Woods Hole registered deep disappointment, too, maintaining the French assault on the *Titanic* amounted to the disturbance of a gravesite.

Although the U.S. Congress signed a bill in 1986 designating the shipwreck as an international memorial, no treaty between nations resulted. Lowell Weicker Jr., the Republican senator from Connecticut who sponsored the Titanic Memorial Bill, said he thought it was "a shame that what is both a monument and a tomb is to be desecrated by the French."[1]

Sometimes the danger of a discovery is that something previously protected and unknown, becomes the object of misuse. If Ballard has misgivings about opening the door to the *Titanic,* he shouldn't—no more than Columbus should take the blame for smog in New World cities. I hope Ballard is still going forward in his easy-going manner, wearing his perennial baseball cap and avoiding the press.

### Notes

1. "Dive Set for Titanic" (Associated Press, July 23, 1987).

### Suggested Reading

Robert Ballard, *Discovery of the Titanic* (Warner Books: New York, 1987).
Robert Ballard in association with Jean-Louis Michel, "How We Found Titanic" (*National Geographic Magazine,* December 1985).
Robert Ballard, "A Long Last Look at Titanic" (*National Geographic Magazine,* December 1986).
Walter Lord, *A Night to Remember* (Bantam Books: New York, 1955).
Lawrence Beesley, *The Loss of the S.S. Titanic* (7 C's Press, Inc., Publishers: Riverside, Conn., 1912).

*Chapter 17*

*Sir Edmund Hillary*

# Sir Edmund Hillary:
# In the Face of Fear

*The greatest obstacle to being heroic*
*is the doubt whether*
*one many not be going*
*to prove one's self a fool; the truest heroism*
*is, to resist the doubt.*


*— Nathaniel Hawthorne*

S ir Edmund Hillary has always been a mountain to me, I think because I grew up in the shadow of his name. In my youth, Hillary was not a common name for a girl, and I would tell people trying to spell it, "It's just like the man who climbed Mount Everest." The first man to reach the peak of what was known as the world's highest mountain represented the highest conquest of self-doubt. My friend Ted Holcomb recently told me that when he heard the news of Hillary's conquest, "Everyone wanted to be the first up Everest in our hearts."

Because I was Sir Hillary's namesake, and he was my childhood hero, I grew up secretly hoping I could some day climb something big myself. When I was invited to New Zealand in 1984 to participate in a diving congress in Auckland, I half jokingly told my hosts that I would be happy to come, if they could arrange for me to meet Sir Edmund Hillary, if only for a minute, if only to shake his hand. My New Zealand friends did more than that. When I arrived in Auckland they announced that they had arranged a lunch for the two of us in a quiet restaurant where we could talk as long as we liked. I was hardly myself the whole time I was in New Zealand just thinking about this meeting.

At 29,028 feet, Mount Everest is said to be the world's highest mountain, a towering shrine that stretches from Nepal to Tibet in the Himalayas. Named after British surveyor Sir George Everest, the mountain is called Sagarmatha by the Nepalese and "Goddess of the Universe" by the Sherpas. Hillary first saw Mount Everest in 1951, when he accompanied Eric Shipton's British Reconnaissance Expedition with the purpose of finding a route up the southern slope of the mountain to its summit. At the time Hillary was a beekeeper in New Zealand, his native country.

During this preliminary foray with Shipton, Hillary entered the world of the Sherpas, a quiet people living what Hillary called a tough, hard life in Nepal's Khumbu district. The Sherpas have been called the "Tigers of the Snow", and for generations they have earned their living by freighting equipment and supplies over high glaciers and treacherous mountain passes.

Two years later, Hillary returned to Everest, and with his Sherpa companion, Tenzing Norgay, he reached the summit on May 29, 1953. For this feat Hillary was knighted by Queen Elizabeth of England.

After the Everest victory, climbers and trekkers began to flock to Nepal. In the 1960s, Hillary helped his Sherpa friends build schools, hospitals and an airfield. He soon began to notice the irony of such progress, for as more expeditioners poured into the Khumbu district, the demand for firewood and building timber soared. Hillary saw that the area would soon be a treeless desert unless some action were taken.

Approaching his own government for support, he advocated the establishment of the Sagarmatha National Park, where trees would be protected. New Zealand replied favorably to Hillary's proposal, and in 1975 the country sent its first national park advisor to the area. Soon after, there was dissension over the park idea among the Sherpas, who were more concerned about firewood and fuel than they were about conservation. But the friend of the Sherpas has remained hopeful that the park will succeed.

Hillary himself is as large and formidable as his mountain, with a tangled, rough-and-tumble craggy exterior. He is more inclined toward wearing old, baggy sweaters than the suit and tie he wore for our meeting in Auckland.

Although he is easily recognized by New Zealanders, who consider him their national hero, Hillary stood alone in the busy lobby, unbothered, when I approached. We went into lunch, and for two hours Hillary talked about adventure.

In 1953, when he and Norgay became the first men to conquer Everest, Sir Hillary's biggest challenge was to overcome his own fear. This conquest is the backbone of all adventure, of all challenges, he said.

"If people say they're not afraid, they're either stupid or not telling the truth," said Hillary. "You have to keep at it until the fear becomes much more acceptable. You want to overcome it, carry on and achieve, despite the obstacles."

Adventurers, he said, are those people who are willing to put themselves in the face of fear, because they want to challenge themselves. Each adventurer has his own brand of fear to conquer.

He talked about the Japanese climber, Naomi Uemura, who disappeared on Mount McKinley in Alaska while climbing alone. Uemura's trademark was that he

174

*Courtesy of the Royal Geographic Society*

*Tenzing on the summit of Mt.
Everest.*

175

*Sir Hillary below the final summit ridge (below and right).*

undertook difficult expeditions by himself. These feats included a solo climb to the top of Mount Kilimanjaro in Tanzania, a raft trip of 3,700 miles down the Amazon, and a 7,500-mile dogsled trek from Greenland to Alaska. Hillary thought that Uemura was taking risks and that it would "catch up with him," but, he added, he understood why Uemura was doing it.

"He wanted to see what this aloneness would add," he said. "He increased the challenges and his abilities by being alone. You get better by increasing your challenges. Aloneness was his particular challenge."

Step by step, a person can increase the challenges he faces, proving to himself that he can accomplish certain goals. Hillary talked about a Sherpa

176

*Tenzing and Hillary prepare to launch the expedition's second assault (left). Tenzing and Hillary after the summit success (below).*

Courtesy of the Royal Geographic Society

woman who weighed only 73 pounds, but who carried an 80-pound load up a mountain path in Nepal. The fact that she could carry "a good load"—one heavier than her total weight—was her particular challenge.

Without challenges, life becomes boring, said Hillary.

"Life is a constant battle against boredom, isn't it?" he said. "Once you've done one thing, you want to do another."

He said he originally titled his book about the Mount Everest climb *Battle Against Boredom.* His publishers were vehemently against it because they didn't want the word in the title. That book eventually became *Conquest of Everest.* According to Sir Hillary,

. . . .what is boring to one person may not be so to another. What makes some people seek challenges while others sit back is a matter of one's having been born with curiosity, he said. Curiosity must be exercised, however, if it is to be increased and stimulated. The curiosity-stimulation relationship is similar to the link between talent and practice: one without the other adds up to very little.

He idolized climber Eric Shipton because Shipton was a man of "wide experience and tremendous drive"—qualities Hillary admires. "He always looked where no one had looked before. In that sense, Shipton had a greater curiosity than mine. Right up until he died, he had that curiosity."

Determination is an important factor in the exercising of curiosity. As a child Hillary was "very determined" and, to become competent in something, he said, a person has to be determined.

Climbing was something he did every chance he got. "I didn't have talent as a climber," Hillary said, "but I had determination."

He said the main goal in a person's life should not be to become the best of something, but to become competent.

"In America, you have the notion that anyone can be president," he said. "That's pure rubbish, simply because millions of people can't be president. Isn't it far more important to become competent?"

Today's adventurer can go into previously unexplored areas because technological improvements have enabled him to do so, Hillary said. "Techniques have improved so much in every field that the modern adventurer can do things that are harder. On Everest, today's climbers can take different, more difficult routes. There are always more and more difficult routes."

Man can also go farther, deeper, higher, because more is known about human physiology. "The idea now is to climb quickly, as fast as possible," he said. "In the old days we thought to go slow, relax, rest."

Physiologists continue to make new discoveries about man at high altitude, but experience is still the best teacher, said Hillary. He, himself, cannot now climb above 14,000 feet, because he once suffered cerebral edema, a potentially fatal condition brought about by high altitudes.

However, while technological advances have enabled men to do more difficult things, the irony is that the same scientific advances are responsible for making men "soft". Hillary talked about a Russian expedition to Everest in which a communications system was set up from below. The climbers were given instructions as to what loads to carry, where and how to climb.

"It was like a moon operation, but where's the motivation?" he asked. "It was very successful, but to me, it lacked the heart and soul of adventure."

178

Space travel fascinates him, he said. He's wondered for a long time what it would be like to be an astronaut. As an interesting probe into the possible relationships between space and earth exploration, Hillary and Neil Armstrong planned to go to the North Pole together in an expedition to be filmed for television.

Space travel, said Hillary, is very different from mountaineering, in that the former involves team effort and the latter involves individual effort. He still likes the individual effort the best.

Today, he spends much of his time alone, a fact he doesn't particularly enjoy but finds necessary because of an extensive lecture schedule. He also continues to write books about his experiences. One book, *Ascent,* coauthored with his son Peter, took a radically different tack from Hillary's normal adventure themes. The autobiography details the one tragedy in his life that remains unresolved—the 1975 death of his wife, Louise, and daughter, Belinda, in a Himalayan plane crash.

Hillary spends a good part of each year in Nepal, where he helps to build schools for the Sherpas and continues to work on the reforestation program of the region. Addressing the idea that he is giving back to the country that has given so much to him, Hillary replied, "That's rubbish. I'm doing it because the Sherpas are my friends."

The big challenge of today, he noted, is in the area of international relationships. "The things we seem so hopeless at are human relationships, peace, overcoming hunger. We're still lousy at this. The major challenges are here on earth, are between people."

Two months after our Auckland meeting, Hillary was appointed as New Zealand's High Commissioner to India, as part of his country's reestablishment of full diplomatic relations with New Delhi. When I heard that, I was struck by the fact that a major achievement in one isolated discipline can have far-reaching effects across the globe. In Hillary's case, one of the world's most challenging mountain climbs has led to a challenging climb for world peace.

### Suggested Reading

Edmund Hillary, *Conquest of Everest* (E. P. Dutton: New York, 1954).

Sir Edmund Hillary, *Ascent: Two Lives Explored: The Autobiography of Sir Edmund Hillary and Peter Hillary* (Doubleday: New York, 1984).

Sir Edmund Hillary, *Nothing Venture, Nothing Win* (Coward, McCann and Geoghegan: New York, 1975).

Sir Edmund Hillary, *From the Ocean to the Sky* (Viking Press: New York, 1979).

Louise Hillary, *A Yak for Christmas* (Doubleday: New York, 1968).

## Chapter 18

Chris Newbert

# Down the Tubes in Hawaii

*Strike whilst the iron is hot.*

— *Rabelais*

C rawling like a Piltdown man across the floor of a darkened cavern deep inside a Hawaiian volcano, I balanced myself with one hand and carried a flashlight with the other. Underwater photographer Chris Newbert, a National Park Service ranger, and I inched our way deeper into the miniature cave. My hard hat banged on the jagged ceiling. It didn't take long before my hands were ragged from the sharp lava on the floor.

We were exploring the Kilauea Volcano on the big island of Hawaii. A month later, that same volcano exploded with pent-up, molten fire.

During the summer of 1982, Chris Newbert invited me to Kona to explore the lava tubes of Kilauea with him. Lava tubes are veins through which the blood of the volcano flows. Were it not for these tunnels, much of the hot lava spilling from the heart of the volcano would not reach the sea. When a volcano erupts, the lava flows downward and seaward in molten rivers that move as fast as water. The sides of the rivers are the first to cool, forming ridges on both sides that build up until they meet at the top. Thus, an insulated channel is formed, allowing the lava to flow as long as the volcano continues to spill. Some lava tubes are seven miles long—immense subterranean caves that have subsequently developed their own biological, geological and cultural systems.

In the hot island sun, ancient Hawaiians discovered that the caverns of the lava tubes were cool refuges from the heat. The cave entrances are open to the sky because of the ceilings that have collapsed. Moreover, warring tribes built up

*Photo by Chris Neubert*

*The entrance to the tubes requires a climb down a rocky path.*

these entrances with additional rock so that only one man could pass through at a time. The narrow doorway kept an entire tribe from stampeding at one attack.

With a National Park Service ranger as our guide, Chris and I started our project by exploring a dark, volcanic tunnel near the top of Kilauea. The guide called the tunnel a "fresh one", since it had been formed in the most recent blowup. The tunnel was small, spread from the central core of the volcano and only three or four feet from the floor to the ceiling. The entrance is well-camouflaged in an enormous field of pillowy lava that crunched beneath our feet like spun glass.

Crawling inside this darkened cavern, I soon realized how sharp lava can be. In fact, I ripped the seat of my pants with the stuff.

There are two types of lava: a'a' and pahoehoe. A'a' (pronounced "ah-ah") feels like it sounds. As sharp as razors, it could also be called ouch-ouch. The other type of lava, pahoehoe (pronounced "pah-hoi-hoi") is smooth. Outside the cave I picked up a piece of the pahoehoe. It was glassy and interesting. I stuck it in my pocket.

The Park Service ranger proceeded to tell us a funny story about how the *National Enquirer* had run a story on Madame Pele, goddess of the volcanoes. The story dramatized the streaks of terrible luck that befell those who took pieces of

182

Pele's lava. After the article had appeared, the *National Enquirer* received tons of lava chunks in the mail from readers who didn't know where else to send it.

When no one was looking, therefore, I slipped my little lava souvenir out of my pocket, carefully placed it back onto the enormous lava field, and told Madame Pele I was only kidding.

Working from the top of Kilauea, Chris and I explored the other lava chambers between the crater rim of the volcano and the sea. We heard about one that contained a freshwater pond, home for a species of aquatic animal found nowhere else in the world. The pond, we were told, is deep enough to scuba dive in.

Some lava tubes provided habitats for certain insects also found nowhere else on the planet, such as the big-eyed, one-eyed spider. Most of these insects are blind adaptations of their sighted insect cousins living outside in the world of light.

Some lava tubes empty out from cliffs into the sea, and one of these serves as a playground for children who climb into one end of the tube and jump out the other into the ocean below. The lava spills that made it to the seafloor exploded on contact with the water, creating subsea caverns where the marine animals of the night hide by day—squirrelfish, soldierfish, octopus and the regal slipper lobster.

The underwater lava tube Chris and I explored is about four miles south of Kona. Chris found it by locating its cinder cones near the edge of the sea. Outside the cave, the water was very clear, and I could see where the lava had first hit the sea. The stuff had cooled, dried and caked instantly. It had formed a series of big caves, at a depth of 40 feet.

In one cave, our lights illuminated the far corners of the cracks and ledges, where bright red squirrelfishes and soldierfishes (called menpachis) hung suspended, looking at us with their big black eyes.

In another underwater cave, we squeezed through the opening, our scuba tanks banging against the ceiling. An octopus took off, muddying the water. At the back of the cavern was a regal slipper lobster, a cave creature endemic to Hawaii and found mostly in the underwater lava tubes. Its head looks like a lobster tail and its tail looks like a lobster tail, so that the regal slipper lobster looks like it's swimming against itself at all times.

The most dramatic part of our volcanic spelunking centered on the burial caves—the lava tubes in which ancient Hawaiians placed their dead. Deep inside the one called "Cowboy Cave", we documented the scene carefully, Chris with his camera, me with my notebook.

The underground cemetery showed that people were laid to rest within and without burial canoes.

A closer look illustrates that a burial site was used for more than one person (opposite, above).

One solitary figure still retained a necklace completely intact (opposite, below).

*Photo by Chris Newbert*

*Photo by Chris Newbert*

*Photo by Chris Newbert*

184

Photo by Chris Newbert

Photo by Chris Newbert

185

Our guide was a brave man for taking us there. In Hawaii, the burial caves are subject to heaps of superstition. Hawaiians, both ancient and modern, will not reveal such cave locations, because anyone who knows the whereabouts of such a cave is a "kahu"—a keeper of the cave. For a kahu to reveal a burial cave location means the punishment of death by the gods.

King Kamehameha I is buried in a lava tube somewhere on the island. No one, they say, knows where. If someone does know, he is taking his kahu responsibilities very seriously.

Our guide, an amateur archaeologist I'll call "Gordon" (not his real name, because "Gordon" believes in the kahu curse), took us to "Cowboy Cave". This burial cave was so named, he said, because one of the occupants was entombed wearing a cowboy hat, blue bandana and boots. Gordon figured the gods would smile on scientifically minded writers and photographers, however, so he took us to the burial site. It lies near a stretch of coast outside Kailua-Kona that is rimmed by an oddly straight row of palm trees.

The entrance of the cave looked different from the normal pile of lava rubble. The lava rocks seemed too regular, as if the doorway had been built up by ancient Hawaiians protecting themselves from warring neighbors. Just inside the door was an enormous cavern, cool and dark.

Gordon led us inside. The ceiling was at least 40 feet high, an eerie place underground. We walked to the back of the main room, turned our lights on and took a left down a side corridor. Another turn, and we were in a cavern not quite as large as the main hall. It was pitch black.

Shining his light on top of a natural rock shelf to his right, our archaeologist friend showed us the coffin that contained the cowboy skeleton, then went off on his own.

At this point, Chris began fiddling around with his cameras. I carefully perched myself on a ledge with four skeletons stretched skull-to-toebone behind me, and began to sketch where everything was. I looked at Chris, who was on his knees, photographing a skeleton on the floor. He had lit a Coleman lantern to photograph by. The lamp cast eerie shadows against the bumps that stuck out from the lava canopy 30 or 40 feet over our heads. It also created a black shadow behind the bone-white skull that remained in a fixed and permanent grin before Chris's camera lens.

I suddenly saw us both from afar—two people taking pictures and sketching as if they were at a Sunday picnic. I let out a big laugh. The noise set Chris off, and he jumped out of his concentration with a yell. His yell set off a yell in me. Gordon came running. He thought we were in trouble.

No, no, no, we said. We got back to work.

I looked at the cowboy skeleton. Whoever that ghostly range-rider was, I could see he had been given a proper and decent burial. He was dressed to the spurs in his cowboy clothes and tucked away in an open coffin on a rock shelf, deep inside the cave.

On the ledge where I sat, there lay a woman with a shell lei around her neck and high heels on her feet. Another bony figure kept its boots by its feet. I drew everything I could see, trying to ignore the unbreathable stillness of the air inside that unventilated tomb.

In another burial cave the bodies had been placed in canoes for rapid transit to heaven. Usually there were favorite trinkets to accompany the departed, like shell leis or favorite clothes.

Chris and I never finished our documentary of the lava tubes, although we keep saying we will, someday, maybe when Kilauea calms down. He has been on a whirlwind tour of promotion for his enormously successful book, *Within a Rainbowed Sea,* which President Reagan presented to Japan's Emperor Hirohito as a birthday present. I have been running around in circles on other assignments, still ripping my jeans.

That's the way it is with adventure. You have to strike while the volcano is hot. There are many interesting opportunities in life that come your way all the time. If you let these go by without complete involvement, they suddenly become past history. Going back to anything is very difficult because you may miss what is coming next.

From the volcano experience, I've learned now to be thorough and quick when opportunities arise. I regret that Chris and I never finished our exploration of the lava tubes, but I believe that regret focuses too much on the past. As the famed writer Henry Miller once said: Regret, like guilt, is a waste of time.

## Suggested Reading

Christopher Newbert, *Within a Rainbowed Sea* (Beyond Words Publishing Company: Honolulu, Hawaii, 1984).

*Chapter 19*

*Glenn Miller*

# Conclusion:
# The Greek Medallion

*We shall not cease from exploration*
*And the end of all our exploring*
*Will be to arrive where we started*
*And know the place for the first time.*


— *T. S. Eliot*

---

Most of the time our travels and life experiences are not intellectual or planned. Rather they are full of stumblings and chance encounters. Chance itself can be of great use if one can recognize the opportunity that may accompany it.

I think of this as I remember how I started my career, because for a time I thought I would work for an airline. However, before leaving for San Francisco with my new college degree to take the airlines job, I went to Santa Barbara for a summer vacation.

Here, I wandered down Miramar Beach late one afternoon inspired by the sea and the sound of the waves. Suddenly I heard a startling noise that sounded as if someone were strangling. I looked up toward a group of battered beach houses and saw a dark-haired man who looked a little like a pirate, standing on his porch with a garden hose in his hand.

The noise came again. I walked toward the house to have a look, and when I got closer I saw what was going on: the pirate was filling a dinghy with water. The odd noise came from his pet sea lion, which was lounging in the dinghy. The sea lion, being nosed by the man's springer spaniel, was protesting. When sea lions protest, they sound like humans being strangled.

"Hi, I'm Glenn Miller," said the pirate.

I introduced myself; then he invited me onto the balcony to see the sea lion.

Glenn said he was a charterboat captain and that he took scuba divers out to the offshore islands of the Santa Barbara Channel. He told me about his trips,

189

about diving and finding wrecks off Anacapa and Santa Rosa, about seeing Indian skulls and bones on San Miguel, about going into a huge cave on Santa Cruz, about storms at sea. His photograph album contained the most unusual photographs I had ever seen. One old black and white picture showed him diving around the wreck of the *Golden Horn,* which sank off Santa Rosa in 1892. Another showed Indian bones and grinding bowls on a sandy beach at San Miguel. Another showed him playing the part of a fisherman in a Walt Disney film, *The Not-So-Lonely Lighthouse Keeper.* There was another that showed Glenn in his scuba equipment, diving next to a huge, sealife-encrusted paddlewheeler. He explained that the wreck was the *Winfield Scott,* a Pacific Mail steamship that had smashed into Anacapa Island and sunk in 1853.

Without my knowing it, my educated perspective on life was being slowly eroded. I had been sitting in a classroom for four years with my books, and here was someone who was diving around sunken ships. I felt a sudden longing—inexplicable and indefinable. The world opened wide and I knew that I wanted to see it, experience it as fast as possible.

Glenn invited me to go to sea with him the next day. He was going to Anacapa Island, taking a group to the *Winfield Scott.*

I was down at the boat early the next morning. Glenn was already there, and so was his springer spaniel, Mac. We headed out of the Santa Barbara harbor in his 65-foot boat, *Emerald,* and set off in the direction of Anacapa.

Anacapa marks the eastern entrance of the Santa Barbara channel and is actually a chain of three small rocks connected by shallow reefs. The whole chain is about five miles long and averages only a quarter mile wide. The jagged cliffs and razor sharp rocks plunge from as high as 550 feet, with a network of caves carved by the ocean at the base of the cliffs. The *Winfield Scott* was just one of the many ships that had gone to pieces on Anacapa.

As Glenn pulled the *Emerald* into the spot where he wanted to anchor, everyone aboard began climbing into wetsuits, fins, masks, regulators, tanks and weightbelts, then leaped over the side. I borrowed a mask and snorkel and jumped over to watch. From my floating position on the surface I could see divers swimming below me—down, down until they were out of sight. Only their bubbles kept coming up. It seemed so awesome to me that people were actually breathing down there deep and out of sight.

After a while I got out of the water and climbed on top of the wheelhouse, sat and looked at the island, at everything. Seabirds flew everywhere. Western gulls dipped and soared. Pelicans roosted on the rocks. It was the end of summer and fall was in the air. As I looked at the island I felt change close at hand, an expectant feeling that often comes with September around the corner.

As the divers climbed aboard the *Emerald,* they talked about the *Winfield Scott* and its giant paddlewheel. They brought up brass pikes, copper nails, pieces of copper sheeting.

The very next day Glenn was taking another group out to Santa Cruz Island, the island west of Anacapa. He invited me again. It took me less than a second to accept his invitation.

This time Glenn asked if I wanted to try diving for myself. I was elated, thrilled that he had asked. He gave me the equipment and also my instructions. "Don't hold your breath," he said. "If you do, you're dead. Just breathe normally and swim around and you'll have a good time."

He also told me that the way I had to get in the water was to stand up at the rail of the boat and roll over head first. Without thinking that he might be kidding, I did it. I was so eager I would have jumped off the wheelhouse roof with all that gear on, if he had told me to.

I will never forget that first dive. Once I got to about 30 feet I saw colors I had never thought possible in the ocean. There were pinks, whites, magentas, reds, purples, greens, oranges, browns, blues. There were fishes, forests of kelp, soft corals, urchins, seals and eels.

I didn't know it that day, but meeting Glenn Miller on the beach in Santa Barbara changed the course of my life. It changed everything. For one thing I never did get to the airlines. The next thing I knew I was diving for sunken treasure in the Caribbean and writing about the undersea world. I met fascinating people who made their living from the sea, including many of the people in this

*Photo by Bob Evans*

*The Emerald*

191

book. I found myself on a trail that became an inspiration for everything I do and feel, a road to a world that is rich in beauty, science, philosophy and discovery.

Glenn Miller eventually sold the *Emerald* and built the 85-foot *Coral Sea*. With Dick Anderson, he went to the Bahamas in that boat in 1980, with the idea of making another salvage attempt on the *Maravilla*, the Spanish galleon that sank in 1656 on the Little Bahama Bank. On the way to the Bahamas from Santa Barbara, Glenn, Dick and their crew got stuck in Panama with blown-out generators and were arrested by the Colombian government and held at gunpoint. The crew eventually tried to find the still hidden treasure of the *Maravilla* by hiring a psychic.

That is the way it is with treasure. It makes no difference how many times an outing like this runs aground. People like Glenn will always toss caution to the wind, opt for the adventure and go ahead anyway.

In the moments I am worried about security I think of these things and I know that any worrying I might do will be for naught. Momentary setbacks are not only the accepted hazards of adventure, but should be taken as positive signposts to life itself. In thinking about the choice between the safe and the uncertain, I realize that the richest experiences of life are often the surprises we get when we continue past the setbacks, choosing the uncertain routes over safe and comfortable ones.

It was all summed up for me by Dr. Joe MacInnis, my Canadian friend who first dived underneath the North Pole and who comforted Ed Link at the site of the submarine accident which took the life of Link's son. During one visit, Joe took a medallion from around his neck and pressed it into my hand. He explained that while he was on the Greek Island of Mykonos, he had found that medallion. I saw that on one side was a crude, ancient-looking rendition of a boy riding a dolphin, and on the other, an anchor.

Joe said that the medallion had special significance. The anchor represented security and the boy on the dolphin, freedom.

I can remember the next moment as clearly as the instant it happened. I had the Greek medallion in my hand and was looking at it while Joe looked at me.

Freedom or security. Joe wanted to know which one I was going to choose.

# Glossary

---

AIR EMBOLISM: obstruction of blood vessels by gas bubbles. In diving, the term is generally applied to obstruction of a vessel or vessels supplying blood to the brain. The injury generally results from an overinflation of the lungs, as may occur in holding one's breath during ascent from the ocean depths. Gas is forced from the alveoli into the blood vessels of the lungs. The resulting bubbles are then carried through the heart and into the body's arterial blood supply. Death is a common result of untreated bubble-blockage of brain arteries.

AQUANAUT: one who participates in underwater scientific research, diving and subsea activities, especially in extended stays beneath the sea in submersibles and underwater habitats.

ARMADA: a fleet of armed ships; a squadron. Between 1492 and 1830, Spain shipped gold and silver home from its mines in the New World, often aboard galleons and other types of ships that sailed together in such armed fleets.

ASTROLABE: a compact instrument used for observing the positions of celestial bodies, now replaced by the sextant.

AVOCATION: a hobby, work which is not one's primary occupation.

BANGSTICKS: a powerhead weapon used against sharks. By pushing a bangstick against the body of a shark, the force of the contact fires the shell, with the force of the blast directed toward the shark.

193

BARALYME: (registered trade name of the National Cylinder Gas Co.) Baralyme is an absorbent dry chemical that absorbs carbon dioxide from the air supply of a diver breathing from a closed-circuit system. Closed-circuit systems (also called recirculating rigs) recycle a portion of the exhaled breathing gas through a carbon-dioxide scrubber that contains the baralyme chemical. Then the breathing gas is returned to the diver. This conserves a substantial amount of the expensive gas mix used in deep-diving operations. Baralyme lasts from 2 to 10 hours and the chemical is usually changed before each dive. The chemical becomes less efficient in cold temperatures or if it becomes wet.

BEDROCK: the solid rock underlying the upper layers of dirt and soil. In gold-mining operations, the gold settles through layers of loose dirt and rests on the bedrock.

BENDS: (see decompression sickness).

BERMUDA TRIANGLE: a three-sided section of the Atlantic Ocean, with Bermuda, Miami and Puerto Rico as its apexes. In this place mysterious disappearances have been said to have occurred for years. Aviators have been known to lose their bearings suddenly and for no apparent reason. Sailors have vanished without a trace. Some have suggested that the area is where the lost city of Atlantis has sunk, or that it has a connection with extraterrestrial life. The Federal Aviation Agency points out that the Bermuda Triangle is one of the two areas in the world where compass needles point to true north, not magnetic north (the North Pole) as they do everywhere else. If the compass variation is not accounted for, a navigator can be off course by as much as 100 miles.

BIOSPHERE: the sphere of living organisms penetrating the lithosphere, hydrosphere, and atmosphere. Biosphere is understood to mean the part of the world in which life exists, including living beings and their environments.

BLOWFISH: a puffer, or any similar fish that can inflate its body.

BLUE HOLES: underwater limestone caves in the Bahamas, originally carved out by fresh water in the Pleistocene era and now submerged beneath the sea.

BOTANY: the science of plants; biology dealing with plant life.

BOUNCE DIVE: a quick dive, usually with a rapid descent to the bottom and a rapid return to the surface.

# GLOSSARY

CEREBRAL EDEMA: edema is the abnormal accumulation of fluid in the interfibrillar spaces of connective tissues—in this case, the brain.

CETACEANS: an order of aquatic animals, mostly mammals. The order consists of whales, dolphins, porpoises, narwhals, grampuses, etc., all of which have a large head, fishlike hairless body, and paddlelike forelimbs.

CHLOROPHYLL: the green coloring matter visible in leaves and present in all growing plants.

COELACANTH: a prehistoric fish believed to be extinct until one was pulled up in the 1960s in the net of a fisherman working off the South African coast.

CONTINENTAL SHELF: a submarine plain bordering nearly every continent and descending in a sharp slope to the ocean depths.

DECOMPRESSION: to release gradually from pressure or compression. In diving the term is applied to the process of following a specific formula for returning to the surface, wherein the diver stops for specified amounts of time at certain decreasing depths. *Decompression tables* have been formulated by the U.S. Navy. These indicate the amounts of time a diver must spend at specified depths during ascent. The times vary, based on the amount of time he has spent at certain deeper depths.

DECOMPRESSION CHAMBER: (sometimes called hyperbaric chamber). The enclosed cylinder is kept at the surface. In this chamber the diver can be sealed off and repressurized to the deepest depth of his dive. Then he is brought back to surface pressure slowly to allow gas bubbles in the blood or tissue to dissolve.

DECOMPRESSION SICKNESS: (also called the bends or Caisson's disease). The illness or injury results from a sudden decrease in one's surrounding pressure and is caused by inadequate decompression following a deep dive. Bends are caused by the formation of gas bubbles in the blood or tissues during or following an ascent. In this case, the bubbles arise from gas that was dissolved in blood or tissues under increased pressure.

ECOLOGIST: a biologist dealing with mutual relationships between organisms and their environment.

GREAT WHITE SHARK: (*Carcharodon carcharias*). A man-eating shark found worldwide in temperate waters. The great white shark reaches lengths of 21 feet or more. These sharks are brownish gray above and white below. The pectoral fins are tipped with black on the undersides. It is especially characterized by a conical snout and large black eyes. The teeth are large and triangular.

HARD HAT: In commercial deep-sea diving this globe-shaped helmet made of copper is used. Its front window, or faceplate, can be opened and removed by unscrewing. Although rigid, plastic-frame diving masks (such as the Kirby–Morgan "band mask") have come into use in the commercial diving field, hard hats are still used all over the world.

HELIOX: a breathing mixture consisting of helium and oxygen, often used by divers for extended deep excursions. By replacing nitrogen with helium, the divers avoid the problems associated with nitrogen narcosis, or "raptures of the deep". Helium, however, is lighter than nitrogen and causes divers to talk in a "Donald Duck" voice that is difficult to understand. Ed Link developed the "heliox unscrambler" to solve the problem of diver-to-surface communication.

HYDROPHONE: an instrument for listening to sound transmitted through water.

HYPERBARIC: (literally "beyond normal pressure"). Relating to the weight or pressure of the atmosphere as it is measured by the barometer, in relation to diving and decompression procedures. *Hyperbaric medicine* centers on decompression sickness. *Hyperbaric chambers* are decompression chambers.

ICHTHYOLOGIST: a scientist who studies fishes. (*Ichthys* is Greek for "fish".)

ICHTHYO-BOTANIST: a scientist who studies fishes and marine plants.

INGOT: a mass of metal cast into a convenient shape for storage or transportation. The Spanish galleons carried ingots of gold and silver, which were later remelted and cast into coins or other objects.

LOCK-OUT: (submersible/chamber). Any two-compartment cylinder or underwater vehicle in which one compartment is kept at surface pressure while the pressure in the other chamber is lowered to the pressure of the dive. In a lock-out submersible, this allows a diver to open the hatch and swim out (which he could not do if the pressure inside and outside the submersible were different, as the pressure differences would tightly seal the hatch). The lock-out chamber is usually located in the back of the submersible, while the pilot's compartment in front, is kept at surface pressure. This allows the pilot to stay underwater for any length of time without requiring lengthy decompression.

The lock-out chamber works on the same principle: a diver undergoing decompression is taken to a depth equal to his dive, then slowly returned to the surface. If medical attention is needed, however, a doctor could not open the hatch to get inside with the diver, since pressure differences would not allow the opening of the hatch. Instead, the doctor can step into the second, lock-out chamber and be pressurized to the depth of the diver in the first chamber. Then the doors between the chambers can be opened and both diver and doctor are later returned to the surface on a supervised decompression schedule.

MAGNETOMETER: an instrument for measuring the intensity and direction of magnetic forces. The magnetometer is used in treasure hunting to detect metal deposits hidden beneath the shallow seas and sand.

MAMMALOGIST: a scientist in the branch of zoology that deals with mammals.

MANIFESTO: on a ship, a listing of the cargo aboard.

MARINE PARK: an area of reef or sea bottom set aside from commercial exploitation, spearfishing or souvenir-collecting.

MID-ATLANTIC RIDGE: a range of volcanically active mountains which divides the Atlantic seabed in half and which is part of a large underwater sea chain that encircles the Earth.

MOHO: short for Mohorovicic Discontinuity. This is the layer of rock between the Earth's crust and its mantle. The layer, defined by the Croatian scientist Andrija Mohorovicic, is believed to transmit earthquake waves more easily than surrounding materials.

MONTEZUMA: Aztec emperor who reigned over Mexico from 1503 to 1520. He was taken prisoner by the Spanish explorer Cortez, who used him as a pawn for his conquest of Mexico City. In June 1520, when the natives of Mexico City retaliated, Montezuma ordered his people to lay down their arms. Instead, the people attacked him and he died three days later.

NITROGEN NARCOSIS: (raptures of the deep). When nitrogen in the air is breathed under pressure at depths of 100 feet or more, it has an intoxicating effect on the body similar to that of alcohol. It is produced by exposure to increased partial pressure of the nitrogen, caused by an overall increase in pressure as the diver descends. The condition is reversible, disappearing upon return to the surface. Nitrogen narcosis can range from mild impairment of judgment or euphoria (false sense of well-being) to complete loss of consciousness.

PECTORAL FINS: on a fish, the pair of fins in the chest area of the body, corresponding to the forelimbs of higher vertebrates.

PLACER: a place where gold is obtained by washing; an alluvial or glacial deposit containing particles of gold or other valuable minerals.

RAPTURES OF THE DEEP: (see nitrogen narcosis).

RECONNAISSANCE: a preliminary survey of territory to gain information.

REGULATOR: an underwater breathing device for maintaining or adjusting the flow of air equal to the surrounding pressure of the water. The equipment consists of a first stage (the valve assembly to the scuba tank) and a second stage (the mouthpiece).

RIFFLE: any various upraised surfaces, such as blocks or bars, laid on the bottom of a sluice to make a series of grooves that will catch and retain minerals, such as gold, during the washing process.

SHALLOW-WATER BLACKOUT: (also called anoxia or carbon-dioxide poisoning). Carbon-dioxide poisoning usually results from excessive breath-holding or skip-breathing during snorkel or scuba dives. To prevent shallow-water blackout one must breathe normally during the dive. Usually the exposure to fresh air relieves the symptoms of shallow-water blackout.

SLUICE: a long, inclined trough for washing gold-laden earth.

SNORKEL: a J-shaped tube, the short end of which is held in the mouth. The long end protrudes above the surface, permitting breathing without raising the nose out of the water when swimming face down on the surface.

*STURM UND DRANG*: storm and stress (German).

SUBMERSIBLE: a small submarine used in underwater work.

SURFACE PRESSURE: The pressure of air at sea level is 14.7 pounds per square inch. For each 33 feet of depth in sea water there is a pressure change. Therefore, at 33 feet, the pressure around a diver will be 2 atmospheres, or 29.4 pounds per square inch (psi). At 66 feet, the surrounding pressure will be 44.1 psi, and at 132 feet (5 atmospheres), 73.5 psi. This is important to remember in scuba diving, because air in a scuba tank will be compressed by half at 33 feet, to a third of its original volume at 66 feet, and so on. Similarly, if a diver holds his breath on ascent, the air in the lungs will expand as he surfaces.

ZEOLITE: any of a family of hydrous silicates, occurring as secondary minerals in the cavities of lava.

# Index

# INDEX

INDEX

Treasure, 19, 20, 23, 28, 169, 170, 191. *See also* Gold
Treasure Salvors, 30
  museum, 28
Triggerfishes, 139
*Tringa* (submarine rescue ship), 38
Tripod fish, 144
Trout, 3, 8
True, Renate, 152
Tzimoulis, Paul, 16, 62

Uemura, Naomi, 174, 176
Undersea medicine, 38, 42, 44, 46, 68
Undersea Research, Ltd. (Toronto), 42, 47
Underwater films, 84. *See also* Diving, filmmakers; Documentary films; Sharks, films of
*Underwater Guide to Marine Life, The* (Ray), 128
Underwater habitats, 36, 42, 46, 47, 49, 62, 130, 147, 151
*Underwater Images* (MacInnis), 42
*Underwater Man* (MacInnis), 42, 49
Underwater parks, 128, 129
Underwater Society of America, 44, 144
Underwater wildlife reserves, 69
*Underwater World* (Taylor), 90
Union Carbide (company), 46
University of Liege (Belgium), 85
University of Southern Florida Marine Science Institute (St. Petersburg), 149
U.S. Divers (company), 59
U.S. Fish and Wildlife Service, 120
U.S. Forest Service, 135

Vanderbilt, Alfred G., 142
Vanderbilt, Anne, and William, 142
Ventura Harbor (Calif.), 70, 74
Viking ship replicas, 20
Vilma (store owner), 101

Virgin Islands, 157, 160
Volcanoes, 93, 118, 119, 169, 181. *See also* Lava tubes

Walruses, 127, 129, 130
*Wasp* (submersible), 52, 155
Waterman, Stan, 41, 85, 86, 87, 88, 144
*Water Planet, The* (filmstrip), 64
*Waves and Beaches* (Bascom), 21
Weddell seal, 130
Weicker, Lowell, Jr., 170
West End Bahamas, 25
Whale catcher, 85
Whales, 67, 85, 86, 87, 88, 127, 134, 158
  sperm, 131
"Whitey." *See* Sharks, great white
Whittaker, Chris, 13, 14, 15
Windship. *See Alcyone*
*Winfield Scott* (sunken ship), 190-191
"Witchpen" software, 17
*Within a Rainbowed Sea* (Newbert), 187
Woman of the Year (Los Angeles Times), 154
*Women in Sports: Scuba Diving* (Hauser), 148
*Wood, A.B.* (salvage vessel), 38
Woods Hole Oceanographic Institution (Mass.), 163, 164, 170
World Congress on Underwater Activities, 62
"World Without Sun" (film), 62
Wuvulu, 69

Yeppoon (Australia), 78, 93
Yoder, Bob, 120
Yorke Peninsula (Australia), 109
Yuba River, 2

Zeolite, 118
*Zodiac*, 87

209